Jess Vallance

YOU ONLY LIVE ONCE

HOT
KEY
BOOKS

First published in Great Britain in 2018 by
HOT KEY BOOKS
80–81 Wimpole St, London W1G 9RE
www.hotkeybooks.com

A CIP catalogue record for this book is available from the British Library.

ISBN: 978-1-84812-660-2
also available as an ebook

2

This book is typeset using Atomik ePublisher
Printed and bound in Great Britain by Clays Ltd, Elcograf S.p.A.

Hot Key Books is an imprint of Bonnier Zaffre Ltd,
a Bonnier Publishing company
www.bonnierpublishing.com

St. Helens Libraries

Please return / renew this item by the last date shown. Items may be renewed by phone and internet.

Telephone: **(01744) 676954 or 677822**
Email: **centrallibrary@sthelens.gov.uk**
Online: **sthelens.gov.uk/librarycatalogue**

3 1 OCT 2020

STHLibraries   sthlibrariesandarts   STHLibraries

ALSO BY JESS VALLANCE

Birdy
The Yellow Room

PART 1

During which I have an epiphany

Diseased

It was the timing of it all that was so unbearable.

Surely the only thing worse than being struck down by a deadly tropical disease is being struck down two weeks after you finish your exams.

After.

If my face had erupted with gruesome pustules two or three or even six months earlier, I still would've been dismayed, naturally, but at least there would've been a compensatory silver lining where I got to build an extravagant bonfire at the end of the garden and laugh into the sky while every text book, notepad and colour-coded timetable turned to dust, on the very day everyone else in Year Eleven was locking their doors and putting on their comfiest knickers ready for weeks of revision hell.

But no.

It was just my luck that the holiday my parents had taken me on as a reward for the previous six months of exam and coursework horror had turned out to be a death sentence.

My parents had tried to give me a treat and ended up killing me. This was exactly typical of them.

I read the web page – www.diagnose-me.com – for probably the eighteenth time.

Severe skin ulceration
Particularly affecting the nose and mouth
Mutilation of the airways
Liver failure
Death

Death! Could they not have put it a bit more poetically? 'Untimely demise'? 'Sad passing'? Though I suppose that wouldn't really have made it any better when it got down to it.

Just then, my three-year-old brother, Paddy, crashed into my bedroom wearing his Queen Elsa dress. As ever, he was dragging his toy giraffe behind him by its tail. My other brother, Ollie – actual age: nineteen, mental age: nine – had persuaded Paddy that an appropriate name for his treasured companion was Dick. This had led to a whole range of bizarre giraffe scenarios, including the time a Jehovah's Witness had called around and Paddy had decided to push the giraffe's face into her stomach and jubilantly shout, 'I LOVE Dick!'

'Made you a sandwich, Gracie!' Paddy said, placing the plate on the end of my bed before sprinting back out.

'Thanks,' I mumbled, glancing over to see what weird combination of ingredients he'd assembled for me this time.

Paddy had two main interests in his young life:

Dressing as Disney princesses, with particular care

taken to the issue of female underwear. Mum and I both frequently found our knickers screwed up in balls at the bottom of Paddy's bed.

Sandwiches – specifically, making them for other people. In Paddy's world though, any three things piled on top of each other fulfilled the brief. Today's treat was a slice of ham, spread with lemon curd and topped with a raw lasagne sheet. I'd had worse, to be fair.

I got out of bed and went back over to the mirror (coughing all the way – no doubt due to my mutilated airway) to check for any fatal disease developments.

The severe ulceration was plain to see. My skin – from the corner of my mouth all the way to my nose – was so disturbingly blistered and pink that it would clearly only be a matter of days before my whole face started to flake off in chunks. Like cooked chicken falling off the bone is how I imagined it.

I might have been able to tell myself that this was OK – that I could wear a comedy mask or a Tesco bag on my head or maybe just pretend that having no face at all was some kind of feminist statement – if it hadn't been for my startlingly yellow arms and legs. Standing there in my pants and pyjama top, they looked exactly like overripe bananas dangling from my torso. And something I knew for certain was that if you turn yellow all of a sudden it means your liver is finished.

Mental Kenneth who used to live at number fifty-seven went yellow on account of him being a raging alcoholic.

He used to sit in a plastic chair on the pavement with a can of Strongbow in one hand and a cigarette in the other and sing 'I Want to Hold Your Hand' to the neighbourhood cats.

I remember the day Mental Kenneth went yellow because when we'd passed him in the street, Paddy, then a toddler in a pushchair, had screamed loudly and covered his face with his blanket. Mum hurried us off, told me that we shouldn't stare at Mental Kenneth and explained he'd only gone yellow because his liver had packed up from all the Strongbows. Since that day I've been well aware that if you go yellow it means your liver's done for and consequently you're not long for this world (Mental Kenneth died three weeks later).

So that was that. I had the full house of symptoms:

Ulcerated skin

Coughing (i.e. mutilated airways)

Liver failure

It was leishmaniasis. I had no idea how to say it out loud but it would probably kill me before the summer was over.

It was all incredibly shocking.

Urgent Emergency

Leishmaniasis is caused by a sand-fly bite. Sand-flies, I'd read, hung around rubbish and came from Southern Europe. I had just spent two weeks in Spain – undeniably the southerly end of Europe – in an apartment that overlooked four enormous rubbish bins swarming with all manner of insect wildlife. I was no expert on flies and I hadn't exactly got up close to have a look, but I would've put good money on at least one of them being a sand-fly.

You can see how the facts of the situation were inescapable. I didn't want to waste time on denial or hope. One thing about me is that I've always been a realist. Another thing about me is that I have the doctor's surgery saved as one of my speed dial options, for just this kind of eventuality. I decided to make use of this now.

'I need an urgent appointment,' I said as soon as the woman answered.

'Can I take your name and date of birth, please?'

If you asked me to describe the receptionist's tone at this point I would have had to say 'bored'. I'd kept my voice calm when I said 'urgent' because I didn't want to come across as hysterical, but what kind of person hears of an urgent situation and doesn't at least adopt a grave tone and immediately ask what's wrong? But then I suppose doctor's receptionists are used to people phoning up and saying that every little runny nose is urgent so it isn't always easy to recognise those of us with a genuine life-or-death predicament to discuss.

I gave her my details. As I said my date of birth I got a sudden glimpse of the numbers of my tombstone:

Grace Georgina Dart
13th February 2001 – 15th August 2017
A waste of a beautiful talent

I didn't strictly know what the beautiful talent was but that's the point really, isn't it? If one's life is cruelly snatched away when it's only just beginning then how can anyone ever know what beautiful talents would lie forever undiscovered?

The bored receptionist was clearly still having issues grasping the concept of urgent because she said, 'Surgery closes at one on a Saturday. Looks like I can fit you in Monday though.'

You'd think I was making an appointment for a manicure or a palm reading. This was obviously the sad state of the NHS in these modern times. I wished that Mum and Dad had good jobs with private healthcare like Chloe Bright's parents. When she had to have a metal pin put in her ankle she went private and got a luxury room with a view of the sea and a TV where you could order any film you wanted from a panel in the side of the bed. She told me that she'd ended up pulling out four of her stitches with her tweezers so she could stay in an extra night because *The Lord of the Rings* trilogy turned out to be longer than she realised.

'I just don't think Monday is soon enough,' I explained as calmly as I could manage. 'My condition may have deteriorated significantly by that point. In fact, I couldn't say for certain that I will still be alive.'

I could tell the receptionist needed some powerful language like this to jolt her into action.

'May I ask what the complaint is?'

I didn't really want to go into details with this woman when I had no idea of her medical credentials but I could see that this was the only way to get her to take me seriously. The only problem was, I still didn't know how to say leishmaniasis out loud.

'It's a rare tropical disease,' I told her. 'Usually fatal.'

'I see,' the receptionist said – staggeringly, still without any real alarm in her voice. 'If you're really concerned then your best bet might be to go to Accident and Emergency at the Royal Sussex.'

Emergency.

Finally, we were getting somewhere. Obviously I should've said 'emergency' not 'urgent' to start with. That was clearly the code word required to get through the system.

'Can you make me an appointment there?' I asked.

The receptionist laughed! She actually laughed. She sounded more tired than genuinely hysterical but still, there is a time and place for a wry chuckle and I did not think this was it. I seriously wondered if I should spend ten minutes of the little time I had left writing a formal complaint to the Secretary for Health about this woman's attitude to the sickly and unfortunate.

'Doesn't work like that, I'm afraid,' she said. 'Just walk in. They'll see you when they can. You can expect a wait though.'

I said thank you to the receptionist (more than she deserved) and hung up.

A Leak

The hospital wasn't that far away. I could probably even have walked it if it wasn't for my failing health. But it was on the number seventeen bus route so that seemed the best option.

Of course, I did think about telling Mum and Dad or even Ollie about the grave situation to see if they would give me a lift but, believe it or not, without a rock-solid diagnosis in the form of a Near-to-Death Certificate from a fully qualified medical practitioner, I was concerned I may have trouble convincing them of the severity of my condition.

I knew that if I asked them to take me to A&E they would want to know why and that would more than likely lead to unhelpful, naïve and, frankly, disrespectful comments about whether I was quite sure it was 'as serious as all that', et cetera et cetera. It wouldn't matter if my arms and legs burst into flames. They would still insist that it was 'probably nothing' and suggest we 'wait and see' what happens. I could just imagine them all standing around my coffin in the church (closed, so as not to alarm mourners with my ulcerated and disintegrating face), Dad saying to

Mum, 'Still, it'll probably be OK. Let's just wait and see how it pans out.'

Anyway, I quite liked the idea of taking myself to hospital on the bus. I thought it made me sound gutsy and independent. I could see the story as a feature on the local news.

'Meet Grace, the brave teen with only months to live facing her fate with dignity and humour. Welcome to the show, Grace,' Jane Kirkwood would say. (She was always my favourite – kind eyes – so I'd pick her to do my interview). 'So first of all, tell us – is it true that when you discovered you were ill you quite calmly took yourself down to the hospital *on the bus?*'

'That's right, Jane,' I'd say with a brave smile. 'I didn't want to make a fuss. Mum and Dad were busy retiling the en suite. I knew I just had to get on with things.'

Then Jane and Duncan Walker (who I didn't like as much but did at least have nice hair) would look at each other and shake their heads as if to say, 'Blow me down, isn't this girl a marvel?'

I packed my bag with all the essentials you could expect to need for a trip to the hospital to collect a dismal diagnosis:
  – Money for the bus (one-way). On the way back
    I thought I could show them my Near-to-Death
    Certificate and undoubtedly the fare would be
    waived.
  – Raw broccoli to help counteract the toxins in my
    bloodstream.

- A bottle of wee (my own). I expected they would want a sample and I always have trouble performing on command.
- One of Mum's magazines as a little light reading material. I doubted I'd be able to concentrate on anything but there was an article in there about a woman who'd found out her internet boyfriend was actually her dad and it's always cheering to know there's someone in a worse situation than you.

When I got on the bus I quite deliberately said, 'Student single to the Royal Sussex Hospital, please.' I didn't really need to specify my destination, but I was thinking that perhaps the bus driver would take pity on me and at the very least give me a sympathetic and supportive smile. But no! Quite the reverse. He insisted on seeing my student card, which luckily I had, otherwise no doubt the miserable old git would've charged me for an adult ticket. I had half a mind to add him to the list of uncaring professionals I needed to formally complain about. I could put the letter in with the one to the Secretary for Health and ask him to pass it on to the Secretary for Transport.

I'd only been sitting down for a couple of minutes when I noticed the unmistakeable smell:

Wee.

At first, I didn't think anything of it – buses aren't exactly known for their hygiene standards – but then I noticed the woman next to me scrunching up her nose and edging away from me and I realised she thought the smell was coming from me.

And then I realised it *was* coming from me.

Coming from my bag, anyway. I reached inside and immediately felt how damp everything was. I took out my sample bottle and saw there was a tiny crack in the plastic. The bottle wasn't *full* of wee – I'm not a camel, for heaven's sake – but there was certainly enough in there that if I let it carry on leaking into my bag it was going to seriously ruin the lining. Not to mention the broccoli. And more worrying than that was the loss of the important sample. I was very anxious that nothing should delay my formal diagnosis.

I didn't have any choice. I had to hold the bottle in my lap, take off one of my socks and wrap it tightly around the plastic to try to stem the flow seeping out. I couldn't risk putting it back in my bag, even with the crack sealed, so I just had to sit there with one bare foot, holding a bottle of my own wee wrapped in a sock, like some kind of conceptual art exhibit.

The woman next to me got up and moved seats. I couldn't really blame her. I found myself looking forward to getting to the hospital – at least there I knew bodily fluids were better appreciated.

Planning

I've always been a fan of a plan. The future, after all, wasn't just going to take care of itself. Without a bit of planning, you were quite likely to rock up in a few years' time and be rather irritated that past-you hadn't bothered sorting things out properly.

My approach had always worked out quite well and had brought with it some not insignificant benefits.

For example, when we went camping at Clatterbury Ring in Year Nine, I was the only person who thought to carry a miniature fire extinguisher in my rucksack at all times. Gregory Short and a few of the others thought it was completely hilarious when they saw it, and called me Fireman Sam for the whole week, but it turned out not to be so silly when sparks from James Handley's campfire landed on Lily Colter's hair extensions and the whole lot went up like a flare. I was able to put my hand on my extinguisher at once and have the whole situation dealt with in a matter of seconds. It would have been a very different story if I hadn't brought it. It would also have been a very different story if Lily had been wearing her hair extensions at the time, as she spent the rest of the evening tearfully telling us.

My future focus meant that I'd always got on quite well at school, despite being, as Mr Murray, my Year Seven maths teacher, put it, 'prone to neuroticism and lapses in logic'. This is because schools, as you might have noticed, are quite futurey places. I don't mean futuristic – Our Lady of Fatima High School probably hadn't had so much as a new netball bib since the 1970s – I just mean that the whole set-up is geared around what's coming up. You're probably familiar with the kind of thing:

Do your homework and do well in the lesson next week.
Do your revision and get a good grade in your exams next summer.
Do well in your exams and get a good life.
All that.

Schools, when you think about it, are just great big future-planning factories, and I had my future plan all worked out.

I would get good GCSEs – mostly As and 8s or 9s if all went as it should. Then I'd start A levels, and do my best with those too. I probably wouldn't get As but I'd try really hard for Bs. After this, I would go to university. I wouldn't get in to Oxford or Cambridge, I'm not unrealistic, but I'd aim as high as I could. Bristol, maybe if I put the work in, or maybe one of the London ones. After that, I would get an entry-level job, probably in London. Or perhaps I'd do an internship or a training scheme. If I had to, I could work in a bar in the evening to earn enough money for rent and everything. I would wear a smart pencil skirt and shoes with a not-too-high heel and people would know they could rely on me to get the job done and they'd call me a rising star of the business world and I'd appear on lists on business blogs called things like '*Thirty under thirty: ones to watch*'. I wasn't sure what business I would be in exactly but that hardly seemed to matter. I would start drinking coffee out of cardboard cups and walk briskly though busy stations tutting at tourists and I would go for after-work cocktails on a Friday.

I had it all worked out.

Don't get me wrong, my meticulous planning didn't mean I always had an easy time of things. Years of intense focus meant I only really had one friend to speak of – Matilda 'Til' Romero – and even she would tell me I was annoying her at least nine times a day.

I also didn't always find the work easy. The last six months of Year Eleven had just about broken me, but as my form tutor Mrs Palmer liked to say, what I lacked in ability I made up for in organisation. Mum was outraged when she heard about that but I took it as the highest compliment. Anyway, I hadn't minded the extra maths study sessions, the early-morning revision club, spending every weekday night locked in my room with index cards and coloured highlighters and every Saturday afternoon in the library, because I had my eyes on the prize. The prize being a dazzling future of smart shoes and corporate networking.

But the uncomfortable truth was that, as I wheezed and coughed and dragged my luminous arms and legs through the wheelchair-sunbathers of the hospital car park, I suddenly didn't know if I had a future at all.

There I was, forced to confront the possibility that every minute of it – every underlined paragraph in my history text book, every French verb list stuck to the back of the toilet door, every text I'd sent saying I couldn't do something because I had to revise – could have been for nothing. I'd spent most of the last sixteen years setting myself up for a sparkling, successful life but maybe it was about to turn out that those sixteen years were it.

They *were* the life.

Immoral Support

'Oh *god*!' I found myself saying it out loud and making an old woman with one leg jump and nearly topple off her crutches.

I'd thought I'd had forever. Well, not forever and ever, obviously, but more time than I could imagine. I'd honestly believed if there was somewhere I wanted to see, I could see it. If there was something I wanted to learn, I had all the time in the world. There were billions of people out there and I assumed that by the time I was done on this planet, I would've met a good chunk of them. I'd always thought there was plenty of time for all of it.

But I'd been wrong.

I stopped outside the hospital entrance and leant against the wall. The summer sun was warm on my face but I was cold inside. Would this be my last summer, I wondered.

I suddenly needed someone to talk to. I'd wanted to be fearless and independent but I just wasn't sure I was up to the role.

I took out my phone and dialled Til's number.

'Yeah?'

That was how Til always answered the phone. I don't

think I'd ever actually heard her use the word 'hello'.

'Til, it's bad news.'

'Yeah, I know. It's rubbish, ain't it.'

That threw me. How could she already know? 'But I haven't told you what it is yet.'

'Yeah, but you said it was bad so I was trying to be sympathetic. You're always telling me I'm not sensitive enough. I'm trying my best.'

'Right, yeah. But, Til, listen. I might be dying.'

'How's that, then?'

'I have a disease. It's tropical. I've turned yellow. I'm at the hospital.'

'Are you wearing one of those paper dresses that shows your bum?'

'What? No. I haven't gone in yet. I'm going to have some tests. And then they might tell me I'm dying. I wanted you to know. As my best friend.'

'As your only friend.'

Why had I thought phoning Til was a good idea?

Til and I had been best friends – of sorts – since Year Eight. We'd been sat on neighbouring desks in science and as we both found the subject at once mind-numbing and incomprehensible, we spent most of each lesson having whispered conversations and sharing bags of Maltesers from the vending machine while Til sketched cartoons of our classmates and teachers on the inside of her folder.

I thought she'd hated me at first but after a year or so of her withering looks and weary sighs I realised that was just how she was.

'I don't hate anyone,' she told me once. 'I mean, they annoy me, sure. You annoy me, defo. But hate? It's just too much effort for someone like me.'

'What do you mean, someone like you?'

'I'm apathetic,' she said.

'A pathetic what?'

'No, apathetic. Chronically unenthusiastic. It means I just don't care, basically.'

Til might not have cared about me, but she did at least hang around with me every lunchtime and most weekends when I wasn't studying so she at least found me bearable. And I could be quite annoying so I was happy to settle for that for now.

'You're not actually dying, right?' To be honest, I thought Til sounded more irritated than concerned, but maybe I was doing her a disservice.

'I'm holding a bottle of wee and it's leaked on me.'

She laughed. 'Rank.'

'I'm going in now. I'll phone you after.'

'Cool, sure thing.' She hung up. I'd never heard Til say goodbye either.

Diagnosis

I went through the big glass doors and headed over to reception. On the bus on the way there, I had reasoned that as my main symptoms – my disintegrating face and my radioactive arms – were clearly on show, the receptionist would be quite likely to realise the urgency of the situation at once and fast-track me to some kind of tropical disease isolation chamber.

Once again though, I was let down.

'How can I help you?' the man on reception said with a smile.

I thought it was perfectly obvious that my body was seizing up before his very eyes, but I supposed he'd been trained that it wasn't polite to comment on people's afflictions, no matter how disturbing the scene.

'I'm seriously ill,' I told him.

'I'm sorry to hear that,' he said, as if he was a waiter and I'd complained about a hair in my soufflé. 'What are the symptoms?'

I resisted the temptation to say, 'Are you blind?' and kept my voice calm and composed as I listed everything clearly.

'My airways are mutilated, which is giving me a painful throat and persistent cough. My skin is ulcerated – as you can see – and my limbs are jaundiced – as you can also see.' I indicated both ulcerations and jaundice in the manner of an air stewardess pointing out emergency exits. 'I suspect the disease is tropical in origin.'

The receptionist frowned slightly. 'Have you travelled recently?'

'Yes.' I told him. 'Only two days ago I was in Alicante, Spain.' Then I added, 'Southern Europe,' just to help him make the connection with the sand-flies, et cetera.

'Yep,' he said. 'I know where Alicante is.' He was being breezy, that's what it was. Pleasant and smiley and *breezy*. I thought it was most inappropriate.

And then I was completely taken aback when, instead of paging the tropical specialist at once, he handed me a form and a pen and said, 'You'll need to register, then I'll get someone to assess you.'

The form was completely mundane with all sorts of irrelevant, trivial questions that really did not seem like a good use of my remaining hours on this planet.

What's my name, what's my address, do I smoke, how many units of alcohol do I drink a week – all this. I was there about a serious medical matter, not to sign up for internet dating, for goodness' sake. Yet another sign the NHS was falling apart, I thought to myself.

Once I'd filled in the form, the receptionist told me to take a seat as there would be a short wait. To my mind, a short wait is what you have while the kettle boils or while an unwanted visitor gives up waiting for you to come to the front door and you can stop hiding behind the sofa. A short wait is minutes, not hours. And definitely not three hours and forty-seven minutes, which is the exact amount of time I spent sitting in a blue plastic chair trying not to pick my ulcerated face and clasping a sock that smelt of wee.

Anyway, I shan't go into the details of all the times I asked the receptionist how much longer it would be, only for him to say (i.e. lie) 'not long now', or the number of times I had to glare at the small child who kept rudely staring at my afflictions while I was minding my own business nibbling on my raw broccoli. What matters is that eventually, a nurse who introduced herself as Claudette, took me behind a curtain, sat me on a wheelie bed and told me she was going to do something called triage on me.

'Is that like mouth-to-mouth resuscitation?' I asked. I didn't really fancy the idea of getting so intimate with Claudette so soon after we'd met but part of me was pleased that some drastic action was finally being taken.

'Oh, no,' she laughed. 'It's basically medical speak for "find out what's going on".'

'Well, I can tell you, if you like,' I said. 'I mean, if it would speed things up. They do say that patients know their own bodies best, after all.'

'OK, sure,' she said. 'Tell me what you're worried about.'

I don't know if it was the way she sat back in her chair looking all peaceful and ready to listen or if it was just the stress of the day finally getting on top of me but I suddenly came over like I was in therapy. I lay down on the wheelie bed like it was a psychiatrist's couch and told her all about our family trip to Spain and the bins and the flies and my ulcerated face, my mutilated airways and my jaundiced skin that was undoubtedly a sign of my malfunctioning liver. Although I knew it was going slightly beyond her remit as a doctor of the body (and not of the mind) I told her what horrendous bad luck it was that I should be dying after my exams and not before.

'The most infuriating part of it is that I don't think I can even say for certain that I enjoyed the holiday! It's very hard to just relax on demand, isn't it? I'm sure you find the same, being an incredibly busy medical professional and everything. People like us can't just flick a switch! I was lying on the lounger and looking at the sparkly sea and saying, "Aaaaah" and "Oh yes, this is the life" and doing all the things you're supposed to do to relax but I just couldn't get into it properly. I kept thinking of what I was going to do next or what I was going to do when I got home or trying to work out what I was going to say when the man with the gold teeth from up the beach tried to sell me a pair of fake Ray-Bans. In fact, I spent quite a lot of time trying to take the perfect photo of myself relaxing on the lounger so I could put it on Instagram and Snapchat to show everyone at home just how comprehensively I was relaxing, but by the time you've factored in showing them that you're wearing a bikini but not showing them all your half-naked flesh, and demonstrating that the weather is glorious and tropical but without looking like a pink, sweaty mess, you can spend half a day just getting that one shot! Anyway, I digress. My point is that, relaxing or not, I went on the holiday and that's how I've contracted this disease. I can't exactly pronounce the name of it but it begins with L and has lots of Ss in it. Probably if you just put sand-flies and mutilated airways and death into Google it will come right up.'

'Leishmaniasis,' Claudette said suddenly.

'Leash your what?'

'Leishmaniasis,' she said. 'What you're describing. You don't have it.'

'What? I – what? I do.' This was all moving too quickly for me. I had put a lot of time into researching my condition and I wasn't sure it was really this 'Claudette' character's place to be making sweeping statements like 'You don't have it'. Not without some careful examination, anyway.

She was shaking her head. 'Nope. You definitely don't. I've seen it a couple of times and that irritation on your face is not it.'

Suddenly I remembered the sample I was clutching. I felt she should at least test that.

'I brought urine,' I said, and thrust the bottle towards her, sodden sock and all.

'Goodness. How organised.' Claudette's nose crinkled very slightly as she took it from me and placed it on the desk in front her. Frankly I expected a higher tolerance from a nurse. Surely one of the reasons a person gets into medicine in the first place is because they have an insatiable curiosity about unsavoury substances.

'You should test it,' I prompted, although to be honest I thought that should be perfectly obvious.

'I don't need to,' she said. She was still wearing that smile. Someone should tell her that smiling isn't always polite, I thought. Maybe it was her idea of a good bedside manner but sometimes a bit of gravity is called for.

Then she took a little torch out of her pocket and said, 'I'd just like to take a look at your throat, if you can open wide for me.'

Sure, I thought, as she went in. I hope you're prepared to see some serious mutilation.

She had a little poke about with her torch and a metal stick thing and then she sat back in her chair.

'OK,' she said, typing a few things into her computer. 'I'd say there are a few things going on here.'

Oh god, I thought. A few things. More than one tropical disease? Surely not.

'You've got a little bit of inflammation in your throat. No more than a cold, I shouldn't think. Drink lots of fluid and take paracetamol. The blistered area on your face is the herpes simplex virus. A cold sore, in other words.'

'Herpes!'

If anything this was worse than a tropical disease.

I had a sex disease!

On my face!

People would think I had been . . . I don't know. Rubbing my face in sex.

'Herpes simplex,' she said again. 'A cold sore. It's quite common. It'll clear up on its own soon enough, or you can get some cream from the chemist.'

'But, I haven't been . . .' I wasn't sure how to put this.

'Herpes is from sex and –'

Claudette laughed. 'This is HSV-1. It's different from genital herpes.'

Genitals! She said genitals. How had this happened? We were meant to be talking about my mutilated airways and now we were talking about genitals and sex diseases.

'How would I have got it?' I felt myself reaching up to cover the blisters with my hands. I was suddenly deeply ashamed of them, sitting there, all sex-diseased on my face.

Claudette shrugged. 'Any contact with the virus. Kissing . . .'

I made a face. That was not something that had happened recently.

'Sharing a cup with friends or family members . . .'

Great, I thought. So that was it. I'd caught it from sharing the toothpaste mug with Dad. I'd got a sex disease

on my face

from my dad.

I still felt there was a fairly major issue that Claudette seemed to be overlooking.

'I'm still jaundiced,' I said. 'So my liver must be diseased. That's my most serious symptom.'

Claudette frowned a little, then she came over and lifted up one of my arms. She ran her fingers over it then – weirdness beyond weirdness – she lifted it up and *smelt it*.

Suddenly I wasn't sure if Claudette was a real nurse at all. First there was the squeamishness around a perfectly naturally (albeit slight leaky) urine sample, then she'd started talking about genitals, and now she was outright sniffing my limbs! She was clearly one of those bizarre fetishists and had snuck into the hospital just to rub her nose on body parts and other such oddness.

'Dihydroxyacetone,' she said, letting my arm go again. 'That's what I think that is.'

I felt my eyes widen. 'Is it terminal?'

Claudette laughed. 'It's not a disease. It's a chemical. It's what they put in fake tan to colour the skin. That biscuity smell is what happens when it reacts with the top layer of skin.'

I looked at my arms. 'I haven't used fake tan. I don't. As a natural redhead, my colouring doesn't carry a tan well. I prefer to stay fair. Like a delicate porcelain doll.'

Claudette frowned slightly. 'Well, that's what it smells like. And that would certainly explain your . . . vivid skin tone.' She smiled in the way that people do when they're trying not to smile, like their lips are being tugged upwards by tiny invisible threads. 'I think you might be right when you say you don't carry a tan well.'

'Well, I haven't used fake tan. It can't be that. Unless someone has come into my bedroom in the night and fake tanned me without my consent, which is a very strange thing to do. Although nonetheless disturbing.'

'What about moisturisers? Any other products that could contain dihydroxyacetone?'

I shook my head firmly. 'No! I –'

Then I stopped myself. Due to a lack of funds, and a lack of inclination to walk all the way to Boots, I had for the past four days been sneaking Mum's body lotion into my room after my shower in the morning.

'Radiance,' I said quietly.

'Pardon me?'

I looked up at Claudette. I could feel my cheeks turning pink, which no doubt was setting off my yellow arms a treat. 'It was called Radiance. But it just said it would give me a healthy glow!'

Claudette smiled again. She didn't even try to hide it this time. 'Well, it's certainly a glow.'

'So, just to confirm,' I said. 'What you're saying is that I'm not in danger of an imminent and painful death?'

Claudette shook her head. 'I shouldn't think so. A cold sore and a cold, that's all. They've probably struck at the same time because you were tired and run down after your exams.'

I felt very small indeed.

I thanked Claudette for her time and bolted through the hospital curtain before I could be diagnosed with any more sex diseases and before Claudette could smell any more of my limbs.

A Wake-Up

It was only when I got outside that the reality hit me:

The bad thing about being told you're not going to die from a tropical disease is that you feel quite silly. The good thing about it, though, is that you're not going to die.

I wasn't going to die. Not any time soon anyway.

I had to phone Til at once to tell her the good news.

'Yeah?'

'Til. I'm not going to die!'

'No? You get tested then? You give them your wee?'

'Yes. Well, sort of. I mean, I'm not *well*, obviously, but I'm not dying. That's the main thing.'

'How do you mean "not well"?'

'I have a bad throat. And a cold sore.'

'Didn't you say you'd turned yellow? What's that about?'

'Tell me, Til. Do you think it's ethical or sensible or legal for a company to just slip fake tan into a moisturiser without being quite explicit that that's what it is?'

Til was already laughing. 'No way. You did *not*.'

'It's actually not funny when you think about it.'

'Tell me you have *not* just been to casualty to tell them your fake tan has gone wrong. That is too good.'

I ignored her. 'I'm serious, Til. Think about it. They put a chemical in their product that changes people's skin! Changing people's skin colour without their consent is assault! Or vandalism. Vandalism of the skin! It's not OK, anyway.'

Til just carried on laughing so I hung up on her to annoy her.

The bus wasn't due to come for another twenty minutes so I decided to walk home. I turned off the busy main road and into the park. It would take ten minutes longer that way, but I didn't care because suddenly, I wasn't running out of time. I had all the time in the world!

I had been given a second chance!

Just five hours earlier I'd been thinking about all the things I'd never get to do – I'd never visit New York, never ride an elephant, never learn to play chess or speak Mandarin. I mean, some things I wasn't that bothered about – chess always seemed a very dreary way to spend time – but the point was, it was up to me again. If I wanted to waste four hours shuffling little bits of wood around a chequered board with a bearded Russian then I could.

A whole day of thinking about how I'd spent most of the last six months – locked in my room in the dark, hunched over my desk, listening to music that sounded like whales having orgasms because it apparently 'aided concentration' – had been an alarming wake-up call.

I was only going to be sixteen once. I would be seventeen in a few months. And then a few months after that I'd be eighteen. All these ages – my youth, my best years – weren't going to last long, and what the hell was I doing with them? I had voluntarily spent fifty per cent of being sixteen listening to whales having sex and doing other things that actively brought me displeasure.

What are you doing, Grace?

What are you doing with your life?

The Epiphany

I'd heard all the sayings, of course, all the motivational slogans – 'you only live once', 'carpe diem', 'live for the moment' – but I'd never really taken in the words before. They were just things that people put on bumper stickers and fridge magnets that didn't mean anything. Just like 'believe in yourself' or 'shoot for the moon – even if you miss you'll land among the stars'.

I mean, honestly. Repulsive, the lot of them.

(And, as I frequently liked to point out, that stars thing makes no sense at all. The nearest star to the moon is 93 million miles away so if you landed among them you should probably give up shooting altogether.)

But suddenly I was seeing these words for the life-changing messages they really were.

You *do* only live once.

I *will* only have this day – this being sixteen and five months and two days – once. Tomorrow it will be gone.

I was taken aback by the monumental profoundness of the realisation. I was having an epiphany, right there, standing in Queen's Park, watching a duck eating a samosa by the pond.

I heard laughter coming from my left, across the other side of the water. I looked over and saw a group of four people probably a few years older than me. They seemed to be some kind of care-free bohemians, with dreadlocked hair and coloured skirts and no tops (the boys had no tops, not the girls. They weren't that care-free).

One boy was juggling with floaty bits of coloured fabric. A girl was poking a small campfire (technically not allowed in Queen's Park – more evidence of their care-free nature, I suppose). They were tanned and laughing and quite obviously beautifully untroubled.

Before my near-death experience, I probably wouldn't have thought much about the people at all, but if you'd asked me, I suppose I might have guessed they were rather disorganised, perhaps a bit lazy and probably never going to do much with their lives. But looking at them now, still in the midst of my life-changing epiphany, I could see that the reality was that it was me who was never going to do much with my life. Not at the rate I was going, anyway.

When we'd gone to Thorpe Park in the spring for my belated sixteenth birthday celebration, I'd left early because I wanted to get a good night's sleep so I could perform to the best of my ability in a history test. I'd spent the whole day barely listening to anything anyone said to me because I was so busy trying to make sure I could list all the key elements of Roosevelt's New Deal. In fact, so distracted was I, that as we reached the pinnacle of Nemesis Inferno and everyone else screamed in delight in anticipation of our fast descent, I'd found myself shouting out loud the words 'Agricultural Adjustment Act'.

But it turned out that it wasn't even a proper test. It didn't count for anything at all. One of the questions was to make up an amusing mnemonic to help us remember the names of Roosevelt's main critics, and the only criteria for getting the mark was if Mr Day thought it was funny enough. An utter waste of time.

When I'd been going around cutting short milestone birthday celebrations for that kind of inconsequential nothingness I didn't see how I'd ever had the cheek to think that the free-spirited jugglers were wasting their lives. If anything these people should be my idols. My inspiration.

I watched them a while longer. I imagined what their lives were like. They were definitely outside a lot; you could see that from their skin. They probably travelled to places like India and Peru and made friends with people they met in hostels and stayed up late playing ukuleles and cooking noodles over camp fires. They probably did something new or interesting every day. They probably never got cold sores on account of being so stressed about trying to memorise a list of alkali metals for some stupid science exam. They probably didn't accidentally paint themselves yellow and then bombard pleasant nurses called Claudette with tedious details about their summer holidays because they assumed they were dying. They probably learnt languages by striking up conversations with friendly, crinkly-eyed old men selling street food from a wheelbarrow, not from staring at a list of verbs they'd pinned to the back of a toilet door. These people probably never worried at all. They probably never had time to worry about life because they were too busy living it.

And so I decided, then and there, that's what I was going to do too.

I was going to start living.

PART 2

During which I am care-free and luxuriate in hedonistic pursuits

The Ultimate Bucket

'Yeah?'

'Til, do you want to ride a horse along a deserted beach with me? Maybe without a saddle. Health and safety dependent.'

'No. Yeah. Maybe. Why?'

I'd been buzzing with the excitement of my epiphany all the way home. Today was the first day of the rest of my life! That was another saying that once would've made me roll my eyes and/or puke in my own mouth but now seemed to be written just for me.

It was the sheer endless possibility of it all that I was quite overcome with.

And it was actually the perfect time for me to have an epiphany, with eight weeks of glorious freedom stretching out in front of me. Now, more than ever before, I was free to do anything!

I felt a sudden compulsion to share my resolution with the world. I reached for my phone and typed a tweet:

Life starts here!

I probably sounded mad. Or drunk. But then on the other hand, social media was full of giddy, jubilant posts from students up and down the country, all on an end-of-exams high.

I was sure that from this moment on I was going to seize every day. I was going to squeeze every minute for everything it had to give. I would try things, do things, have experiences. I wouldn't turn down a single opportunity. But I knew I couldn't sit around and wait for opportunities to come to me. Otherwise I might not get an offer any more exciting than extra cheese on my Subway. I was going to have to go out there and find things. Create opportunities.

It was almost too much. I didn't know where to begin. When the whole world is a collage of experiences, of which you've had basically none, how do you choose which experience to experience first?

I turned on my laptop and ran a few searches:

Experiences

Things to do

Things to do before you die

After scrolling past a few websites selling corporate team-building activities and promoting stag dos, I found a site called 'My Ultimate Bucket List'. It was a list of 1001 things everyone should do at least once in their lives. It was exactly what I was looking for.

I didn't want to spend too long examining every activity. Partly because sitting at my desk squinting at my laptop screen was exactly what I didn't want to be doing now I'd been reborn, but also because I planned to get through a good chunk of those 1001 things eventually anyway, so it didn't matter where I started.

I scanned down the list.

Give money to charity

I wasn't sure that was officially an 'experience', was it? I could easily drop a pound into the collection pot at the end of the till at Sainsbury's if I wanted to check something off the list, but it wasn't really what I had in mind.

Tell someone you love them

Oh, please. Who would I be saying it to? Mum? Where was the excitement? Where was the stuff I could take photos of myself doing to show everyone how I was really *living*?

Then, there it was, coming in at number forty-five.

Ride a horse along a deserted beach

Now *this* was what I was talking about.

I could imagine it already – the sunset, the sound of the waves lapping the shore, the gentle breeze giving my hair a relaxed, tousled look as I expertly guided an elegant mare called Ebony or Clementine across the unspoilt sands. It would be the perfect start to my new life. And it would be the perfect scene for some attractive photos that I could post on Twitter and Instagram and Snapchat to show everyone that yes, I *had* been boring, I *had* been focused on school because that's what I'd had to do, but now that was over, the real me could emerge – and the real me was fun and wild and care-free and having an amazing time.

The Plural of Sand

As brave I was feeling in my new role, I couldn't help but think it would be more fun if I had someone to share my inaugural spontaneous experience with. I also needed someone to take the photos. All I had to do was convince Til what a good time we'd have.

'I just think it sounds amazing, don't you?' I gushed. (I'm not sure I had ever gushed before.) 'Galloping through the sands, not a care in the world, not a living person in sight. Well, except for each other, I suppose.'

'Dude, it's summer. The weather's lush. The beach is going to be packed with kids and tourists and just about everyone from our school getting wasted on warm white wine.'

She had a point, but I wasn't deterred. 'OK, so maybe not this beach. Maybe not Brighton beach. That wouldn't work anyway because it's stones, and I feel quite strongly that we need unspoilt sands. But we can find one, I'm sure. We can find some sands.'

Til wasn't exactly buzzing with enthusiasm but then if it was enthusiasm I was looking for, Til probably wasn't the first person I'd go to. 'Why do you keep saying "sands"?'

she said. 'Ain't the plural of "sand" just "sand"? Unless you're the Prince of Persia.'

I ignored this question. 'Meet me at the station in an hour.'

'What, we're doing this *today*?'

'Yes!' I said, exasperated. 'Because today is everything. Today is all we've got. This moment. Now or never.'

'Gracie, have you been sniffing your Tippex pen?'

'No. I'll explain when I get there.'

I met Til at the station ready for the 13.04 train to Chichester. After I'd (sort of) managed to rope Til into my first spontaneous experience, I'd done a bit of research and found there were some stables that offered horse rides a short walk away from West Wittering beach, which, according to the tourist board website, had 'an expansive sandy beach' and was in an area of Outstanding Natural Beauty. It sounded perfect for our needs.

I remembered as I looked through the gallery of images on the website that just last term, my whole geography class had been taken on a day trip to West Wittering beach. There was some spurious educational reason for the outing – something to do with grass species and sand dunes – but it was widely acknowledged by staff and students alike that the trip was essentially about having some fun in the sun before the serious business of GCSE revision began in earnest. My fellow students embraced this opportunity fully, but I didn't even entertain the idea of going.

The trip, it was clear, would in no way contribute to my exam grade. There was nothing I would learn by taking a whole day out of study that I couldn't find out from reading two short pages of my text book. In terms of facts harvested per hour spent, it simply did not offer a good return on investment. I'd put this reasoning to Mr Gosport, our Geography teacher.

'That's probably true,' he'd conceded. 'But this is a more enjoyable way of learning the facts, surely?'

This was entirely beside the point. I wasn't interested in enjoying myself! As the rest of my class scrambled onto the coach in a race to claim the back row, I made my way to the library, keen to use the time to get ahead of the rest of the class in my reading.

As we sat on the bench on platform one, I filled Til in on how my near-death experience had spawned a new me – a new outlook, new priorities.

'I'm not being funny though, Gracie, but you didn't actually have a near-death experience, did you? You just have a cold and look rubbish in fake tan.'

I sighed. She really wouldn't let the whole fake tan issue go.

'But that's irrelevant! Can't you see? The point is, I *thought* I was a goner. I *thought* my time was up. Although my body may not have been as near to death as I thought, my mind was. I've had a wake-up call. A brush with my own mortality. It was a gift really, that happening to me. And I don't intend to waste it.'

'Right-oh,' Til said, idly fiddling with her train ticket. She seemed altogether uninspired by my epiphany, it had to be said. 'It *is* about time you chilled the hell out, to be honest. You've been well boring.'

I couldn't argue with that. I had. But not any more. Boring Grace was dead. Killed by leishmaniasis.

An hour and a half later, we pushed open the heavy metal gate that was the entrance to Appleyard Riding Stables. A woman with two long blonde plaits and wellington boots called over to us from where she was tossing bales of hay into the back of a van.

'You ladies OK there?'

'Um . . . yes,' I called as we carefully made our way through the mud and horse poo to where she was working. 'I was wondering if you can help us. We're looking to ride a horse. Two horses, I mean. One each.'

The woman put the last of the hay bales into the van and slammed the door shut.

'Have you booked?'

'No . . .' I admitted. I hadn't even thought of that. Booking wasn't something I thought you had to factor in when you were trying to live a spontaneous life.

The woman looked at her watch. 'We've got a bunch of birthday party kids coming in twenty minutes but you could have a quick go round the field on Bertie before they turn up.'

She nodded over to Bertie – a bedraggled grey creature, swishing his tail to sweep away the flies that were gathering around his bum.

'Well, actually,' I explained, 'we were hoping to go to the beach. To ride a horse – two horses – there? On the unspoilt sands?'

The woman frowned. Then she laughed. 'Oh, were you now? I'm sorry, darlin', but it's not like hiring a carpet cleaner. Horses are living beasts. You can't just take one away with you. I've got to think about their well-being. And yours.'

'Oh,' I said, feeling dejected.

'This is going well then,' Til muttered, poking the mud with the toe of her trainer.

'I can book you in for a taster session if you like,' the woman offered. 'Nothing free till next week though.'

'It's just I was so hoping to ride a horse on the beach,' I said. 'That was kind of a key part of it. The sands.'

Why did I keep saying sands?

The woman went around the side of the van and opened the driver-side door. I got the feeling she was getting bored of us. 'If that's what your heart's really set on, then they do rides down on the beach. Just outside Jumble's Cafe.'

Then she climbed into the van, closed the door and started the engine.

I looked at Til.

'We going to Jumble's Cafe now then?' she said with a sigh.

'We certainly are,' I said, already on my way to the gate.

Nobby, Petal and Brenda

Jumble's Cafe was half cafe – selling ice creams and cones of chips from a kiosk at the side – and half beach shop, with lilos and spades and unattractive plastic sandals flapping about in the wind on the terrace outside.

'This definitely the right place?' Til said as we made our way over. 'Can't see any horses.'

'It says "Jumble's" though . . . That's what she said, isn't it? I'll ask.'

The boy curling ice creams into cones in the kiosk wasn't much older than us.

'Excuse me,' I said to him. 'I was hoping to ride a horse.'

There was a flash of alarm in his eyes. 'I'm new,' he said. 'Only been here a week.'

I was confused. 'Oh. OK. Well, congratulations on your new job. But do you know about the horses? Can we do that here?'

The boy frowned again. 'They do donkey rides,' he said. 'Up the beach there.'

I looked at Til. I wasn't sure donkeys and horses were quite the same thing.

'But no horses?' I said.

The boy shook his head. 'Not seen any, no.'

We thanked the boy and headed in the direction he'd pointed.

'It's basically the same, innit?' Til was saying. 'Four legs, little hooves. Hairy neck-wig.'

'No,' I whined. 'Not really. Horses are magnificent and graceful, and I would look magnificent and graceful on the back of one. Donkeys –'

'Donkeys stink,' Til said, putting her hand over her nose and mouth as we arrived at the spot where six donkeys were mooching around next to two middle-aged ladies sitting in deck chairs. There was a chalk board just in front of them with the words 'Donkey Rides £3' written on it.

The main thing that struck me was just how small they were (the donkeys, not the ladies. The ladies were quite a good size). I suppose it had been a number of years since I'd seen a donkey up close and I must've done quite some growing in that time. As I looked at the hobbity little creatures in front of us, I wasn't even sure my feet would clear the ground if I sat on one.

'Uh yeah, so we want to ride a donkey?' Til was already saying to one of the ladies in the deck chair. She had long grey hair in a ponytail and a translucent plastic sun-visor that meant half her face was bathed in a strange green light. She was wearing a kind of ruffled boob-tube affair, which seemed to be slipping dangerously down her torso.

'Right you are,' the woman said, heaving herself to her feet.

'Wait a minute,' I hissed to Til. 'Do we, though? Do we want to ride a donkey? I wanted to ride a horse. Not a donkey.'

Til put her head on one side. 'Well, there ain't any horses here. So it's donkeys or nothing. Plus, the thing about living for the moment is you have to, like, go with it, don't you? You can't be making rules and listing criteria and wanting everything to be perfect. That ain't the spirit really, is it, Gracie?'

She made a good point. I wanted to seize all opportunities I was given. Grab the life that was thrown my way. And right at that moment, life was throwing me donkeys, so it would be a pretty poor start if I didn't grab one.

'OK,' I said, nodding. 'You're right. It's just . . . I so wanted a photo to mark the start of my adventure. A photo of me on horseback, laughing, with my hair looking artfully dishevelled.'

Til was already rooting in her purse for some change. 'I'll still take a photo,' she said, tipping the change into the woman's hand. 'I'll just get you, and a bit of the donkey's back in it. You won't even be able to tell what animal it is you're sat on. Pretend it's an antelope if you want.'

That sounded more promising.

I followed the woman, who introduced herself as Brenda, over to my steed – a dopey looking animal with a saddle that said 'Nobby' in bright pink paint.

'Here you go then, love,' Brenda said, holding the donkey by his reins while I clambered onto his back. 'You have a little ride on Nobby.'

Out of the corner of my eye, I could see Til trying not to laugh. I glared at her. She'd better make sure Nobby's name tag wasn't showing in the photo.

When Til had mounted her donkey – the much more elegantly named 'Petal' – Brenda asked if we were all set, and we nodded. Then she stood between us, a donkey's rein in either hand, and called, 'Walk on.'

Nobby and Petal dutifully ambled forward, Til and I wobbling on their backs.

I must say, the whole spectacle was quite far from my vision of my horseback debut. We were limited by Brenda's walking speed, and there was no way I was going to feel the wind whipping through my hair with a middle-aged lady in a boob tube setting the pace.

'Do you want me to do the photo then?' Til asked, reaching for her phone.

I shook my head. 'Not yet . . .' I said. Then I leant forward slightly and said, 'Brenda, I was just wondering if we could have a go at riding on our own for a bit? Just so we can pick up a bit of speed?'

Brenda chuckled. 'Oh, I get you,' she said. 'Bit of a dare-devil, are you?'

That was not something I would ever call myself.

'No can do, lovey, I'm afraid. Accompanied rides only. Wouldn't want Nobby and Petal to make a break for it!'

And so on we strolled.

'Shall I just do it then?' Till said, waving her phone. 'The photo? Doesn't sound like we're going to be galloping anywhere?'

I sighed. 'Yeah, go on then. But don't get Nobby's donkey face it in. Or his Nobby name tag! Just me, OK?'

Til held up her phone. 'Smile, then. Look care-free or whatever.'

'Oh, photo op, is it?' Brenda said. And with that she turned to the side and pushed herself up against my right leg. She looked square at the camera and did an exaggerated thumbs-up. 'Cheeeeeese!'

Til gave me a look as if to say, 'Is this what you want?'

I returned one that said, 'Hell no, but what can I do?'

Til took the photo. I'd just have to Photoshop Brenda out. Somehow.

Till looked at the screen and winced.

'What?' I said.

She passed me the phone and I squinted at the screen, holding up my hand to shield it from the sunlight.

'Oh god,' I groaned.

The photo was hideous. My hair – far from relaxed and tousled – had frizzed into a mullet. Brenda's neon-pink boob-tube shone out boldly against my resplendent yellow legs. I'd carefully tried to set my face into the expression of someone having a spontaneous and highly enjoyable experience. I'd been aiming for something between mid-laughter and slight surprise. A look that said, 'I don't know how I ended up here but I'm loving it!' I hadn't quite pulled it off.

'Why are you doing a face like you've got a wasp up your bum?' Til said as I handed the phone back. 'You look insane.'

I couldn't disagree. There was no way that photo was going anywhere public.

Soft

Once Brenda had led us back to the deck chairs, and we'd bid farewell to Nobby and Petal, Til and I sat on the beach and shared a bag of Quavers.

'That was . . . different,' she said.

'Yes,' I frowned slightly. 'Wasn't quite what I planned.'

Til shrugged. 'Like I said, that's the point. You don't get to have everything go to plan any more.'

'I guess,' I sighed. I took my phone out of my pocket. 'Anyway, just because I can't put that photo up doesn't mean I can't say what I've been doing, right?' I typed out a tweet.

'What did you put?' Til asked as I slipped my phone back into my bag. She took out her own phone. '"Amazing afternoon on horseback, galloping through the waves! What a buzz!"' she read out loud. She looked at me, one eyebrow raised. One of her favourite facial expressions. 'Grace? Seriously?'

'I know it's not technically true, but does it really matter?'

'Mate, who cares if it's true or not. The point is, you sound like a plank.'

'Three likes already,' I pointed out. 'I guess some people

like planks.' I sighed and leant back on my elbows. 'It was fun, though, in a way. Wasn't it? Brenda and Nobby and Petal.'

Til nodded as she twisted her crisp packet into a knot. 'Yeah, it was all right. And yeah, actually, it is good. You. Being like this.'

'How do you mean?'

'Like . . . leaving the house. Being up for stuff. Not banging on about practice papers or designated revision breaks. I missed you, man.'

I didn't know what to say. This was hands-down the most affectionate thing Til had ever said to me. It was turning into quite the day.

I just looked at her.

'What?' she said, irritably.

'You never say nice things to me!'

'Shut up,' she said, but she shifted about a bit in a way that showed me she knew I was right. 'You don't always make it easy. You're a pain in the bum. And you didn't come to my birthday.'

I knew she was still stewing about that.

For her sixteenth birthday in May, Til had organised a camping trip to a site in the Downs. I was meant to be going but I'd panicked at the last minute about a history essay and pulled out.

'I'm sorry,' I said, even though I'd said it a million times already. 'Look. I'm free now. I'm *fun* now. Let's do it again. Let's do it at the weekend.'

'You're kidding, right? That site gets booked up months

and months in advance. No way we'll get in. Or anywhere else round here at this time of year.'

I thought for a moment. 'OK, so maybe we can't do that. Not exactly the same. But we'll do something. I'll do something. For you. We'll do something fun.'

Til looked at me, the slightest smile on her face. 'Yeah?'

'Yeah,' I said firmly.

'Cheers, Gracie.' She gave me a soft punch on the shoulder. 'That sounds cool.'

Then she leant back and closed her eyes with a smile. 'Tell you what,' she said. 'That near-death experience of yours has made us soft.'

Hapy Brthdax, Til

I spent the following Saturday morning rummaging around in the garage looking for all the props I needed for that evening.

Today was Til's sixteenth birthday: Part Two. The better part, one might argue, as it would be the part where I was in attendance. After all, new Grace was the life and soul of any celebration.

The garage was a tip because Dad was in charge of it and Dad's idea of being in charge of something was shutting the door on it so he didn't have to think about it.

I was looking for the tent, last seen when Ollie took it to Glastonbury the previous summer. I eventually found it under a giant plastic model of Elvis wearing an apron that said 'All shook up' that Dad refused to throw away in case we needed it. I could not even begin to imagine a scenario where a person would need a giant plastic Elvis in an apron. The tent was a bit dusty but seemed intact, so I tossed it into the middle of the garden and decided to tackle it after I'd been on a provisions run.

I went to the shop and bought barbecue coal, sausages,

drinks and marshmallows. I also bought Til a cake in the shape of a Thomas the Tank Engine because it was the biggest and most expensive one on offer, and now I was living for the moment I didn't think twice about splashing out on novelty cakes and other such frivolities. Also, I'd just realised that, much to my surprise, I was somewhat flush with funds.

For the first half of Year Eleven, I'd worked in Wagstaff's Chemist every Saturday from 9 a.m. till 5 p.m., sometimes on the checkouts, but usually just pulling bottles of shampoo to the front of the shelves to make them look tidy, and generally ambling about, pretending to be doing something useful. This job earnt me the princely sum of £38.50 a week, which was actually all I needed. The only problem was that, as my workload got higher at school, so did my stress levels.

One Saturday, after attempting to stay up all night to finish an English essay and then go straight to work without so much as a catnap, I was so tired that I fell off the bus. I have no idea how it happened. One minute I was upright in the doorway, ready to bid the driver a cheery, 'thanks, bye!', the next I was on my hands and knees trying to push my lunchbox back into my bag while a passing golden retriever misread the situation and tried to mount me.

More from embarrassment than physical injury I decided I couldn't face work that day. I went home and cried to Mum, who said that it was more important that I focused on my exams and that she'd give me £20 a week until the year was finished, to tide me over until I had time to get another job.

Mum and Dad weren't pushy as such, but they were keen

on talking about potential. Dad's job was something to do with computers and trains that he always said was too boring to talk about but he never seemed too worried about whether he'd made the right career choice. Mum, though, always said she wished she'd gone to university. I think she was happy enough working in the sexual health clinic next to the station – 'just on the phones, I keep my hands clean!' as she liked to say – and there certainly seemed to be more freebies than you'd imagine in that line of work. There were so many educational leaflets on the pin board that I think even Paddy could have advised you on the best way to avoid contracting chlamydia. We also had a bowl of condoms in the downstairs toilet where other families might have had pot-pourri. Although who they were for, I have no idea.

I knew I was lucky. In fact, I never told Til about Mum's offer, as I knew she'd roll her eyes and call me a spoilt princess and maybe she was right. The thing was though, as I worked more and went out less, I was barely spending any of the pocket money Mum was giving me. By the summer, I'd built up quite the nest egg.

I spent a long time pitching the tent in the garden, an endeavour that turned out to be even more stressful than the time I realised I had my school shirt on inside out and tried to turn it around underneath my jumper in history, nearly suffocating myself in the process. In the end, Nancy Brewster had had to guide me to the medical room so I could be wrestled free by the school nurse and given a glass of orange squash to calm down.

If it had been any other occasion I would have asked Til over to take charge of the situation. Til was nothing if not capable.

For example, when I'd woken up one Sunday morning with an essay and a lab report to finish, only to find my laptop screen reporting a dramatic 'fatal error' message, I'd texted Til in a panic and she'd told me to come over. When I'd arrived at her flat, I'd found her lying on the floor of her kitchen with her head under the sink, making some kind of adjustments to the pipes with a spanner. The floor was covered with a suspiciously yellowy water.

'What's going on?' I'd said from the doorway.

'Blocked sink,' she grumbled, standing up and wiping her hands on her jeans, before taking my laptop out of my hands and placing it on the table in the lounge. She tapped around on the keyboard for a few moments, turned it over, took the battery out, put it back in, typed a bit more, and then turned the screen around to face me. The normal loading screen was showing again.

'You fixed it?' I'd said, surprised.

'Yeah, course,' she'd shrugged, before heading back to the kitchen to resume her plumbing repairs.

Til didn't manage to completely solve her blocked sink and she'd been forced to call out an emergency plumber at 11 p.m. one Friday. The cost of which had both disgusted and impressed her, so much so that she'd announced the following Monday that she planned to study plumbing at college. I hadn't taken her quite seriously at the time, but the way she was steadily building up a collection of plumbers' manuals and tools told me she meant business.

I found some paper bunting letters that Mum had used to decorate the desk of a bloke at work who was leaving so I decided to make Til a birthday banner. I was a few letters short, so the message that would greet Til when she turned up at our camp was:

HAPY BRTHDAX TIL

If I'd started planning everything weeks in advance, no doubt I would've managed to collect enough letters to spell out 'Many happy returns, Matilda Romero. Have a lovely time', but these are the idiosyncrasies we must accept when we're celebrating spontaneously. I thought she'd get the general idea.

Camp Matilda

Til arrived at seven, as I had instructed.

'All right?' she said. 'You gonna do me a birthday then, is it?'

I nodded. 'Yep. Come, come.'

Til looked at me quizzically and followed me through the hallway and towards the back door.

'Welcome to Camp Matilda!' I said as I opened the back door to the garden.

'Ha,' Til said, dropping her bag to the floor and folding her arms. 'Beautiful work, Gracie.'

I turned around. I think the pole in the middle of the tent must've toppled over, because all the canvas was sagging. With nothing to support it, my banner had dropped on the right-hand side. It looked like a storm had ripped through our camp.

'Oh,' I said, frowning as I struggled to pull the tent upright. 'Stupid thing.'

Til laughed.

'I was recreating your birthday camp!' I said, still trying to get the tent together. 'But now it looks rubbish. Sorry.'

Til came over to help me. 'Ah well,' she said, managing to get the pole back in position. 'The thought ain't so rubbish.'

It had been warm all day. Not perfect blue skies, but fine. Fine for camping. But as Til and I finally set the tent straight, a fat drop of rain splashed off my shoulder.

'Oh, for goodness' sake,' I said, looking up at the sky. 'This was absolutely not forecast.'

'Never mind. That's what the tent is for, I guess.' She pushed her bag through the entrance. 'Oh, you beauty,' she said as we clambered awkwardly through the flap and she saw the cans of Guinness I'd lined up.

Last Christmas, Til and I had gone to a house party that a boy from the year above was holding while his parents were away. We'd asked Ollie to go to the shop to get us a bottle of vodka to mix with the Coke we'd bought, but at the last minute he'd come over all responsible and returned with some cans of Guinness instead. 'Better for you,' he explained. 'And it was on offer.' Without any better options, we ended up taking the Guinness to the party anyway, and we'd found that we'd actually quite liked it. It tasted like a wholesome, robust gravy. And more to the point, we felt that drinking it made us appear interesting and quirky.

Til snapped open two cans and passed one to me. We sat at opposite ends of the tent and sipped our drinks.

I looked around me. 'What else are you supposed to do when you go camping? What did you do on your birthday trip?'

Til shrugged. 'Made a fire, cooked on the fire. Sat around the fire. Played guitars next to the fire. The fire was kind of a thing, really.'

'I planned for that!' I said, putting my can down and scrambling out of the tent.

'Course you did,' Til said, following me. 'Course you did.'

I took Til over to the corner of the garden where I'd stacked logs, newspaper and matches, together with a bag of marshmallows ready for the traditional toasting.

There was only one small problem.

'Oh no . . .' I looked down at the pile of wood and paper. The rain had stopped, but it had obviously been going for long enough to leave my fire-lighting material completely sodden. There was no way any of it was going to be producing a roaring fire any time soon.

'Ah well,' Til said, peeling a sheet of soaking paper off the ground. 'Good thing about garden camping is you're not too far from the oven.'

Queen of Spades

Twenty minutes later, we were back in the tent with hot dogs cooked under the grill and a bowl of pink goo that was the result of attempting to toast marshmallows in a microwave. We decided we'd have to eat it with a spoon.

'Argh!' Til screamed, her mouth hanging open. 'This stuff is like molten lava. You could kill someone with this.'

I passed her a can of Guinness and reached for my own can. 'Now what shall we do?' I said, fiddling with the metal ring pull. 'What are you supposed to *do* when you're camping? Now that the fire's a no-go, anyway?'

Til shrugged. 'Thing is, normally it's all about, like, survival, you know? Spend ages putting up shelter, ages trying to cook food. Keep warm. Stay dry. Just making it through the night kind of keeps you busy.'

I frowned. 'It's a weird thing to do for fun, isn't it? Pretend to be homeless.'

Til nodded. 'Uh huh. And it don't really work when you're ten metres away from a kitchen with a toaster and an electric tin opener and a fridge full of avocado salad.'

I didn't say anything. I suddenly wasn't sure that I'd

created such a good birthday celebration after all.

'Cards,' said Til suddenly. 'We played cards. That's what people do when there isn't any TV or when they're in the war or whatever.'

This brightened me up. Cards I could do. 'OK,' I said. 'Good idea. I'm on it.'

I ran into the kitchen and grabbed the pack of cards that Ollie had left there after his weekend poker game.

'Right!' I said, taking my seat in the corner of the tent again. 'We have cards.' I tipped the cards out of the box. 'I can hardly remember any games though, it's been ages. Only like Snap and Pairs and those boring ones. Do you know an – oh god!' I dropped the pack like it was electrified, letting the cards scatter everywhere. 'Oh god, I didn't know they were going to be . . . to look like . . .'

Til was laughing. She picked up a card. 'You bought porno cards?'

'I didn't! I mean, I brought them out here, but I didn't buy them! I didn't know! They're Ollie's!'

'Yeah, yeah,' Til said, still laughing. 'It's fine, Gracie. You got to get your kicks where you can find them.' She picked up the cards and shuffled through them, having a good look at each one. 'Wowzers,' she said, holding one out to me. 'Queen of Spades *really* likes spades, huh?'

'Oh my goodness,' I said, covering my eyes. 'That is so unnatural. I will never be able to look at a garden spade again.'

'Ah, well,' Til said. 'We can battle through it. Wouldn't want these ladies' hard work to go to waste.'

She started to deal and we did actually become desensitised to the naked bodies pretty quickly.

As Til dealt our second hand, she stopped suddenly. 'Oh, wait,' she said. 'Wait a minute. You didn't do this on purpose, did you? Oh, you did! This was your ice breaker. Your conversation starter. And I've completely missed it. Oh, man! Sorry. You're right. I *am* insensitive.'

I looked at her. 'What?'

'You got these cards on purpose because you want to talk. You wanted to bring up the whole lezzer issue and you weren't sure how, so you thought you'd "accidentally" whip these out and I'd take the conversation from there.'

I opened my mouth and closed it again. I felt my cheeks flush. 'What lezzer issue?'

Til put the cards down and sat facing me square on, her hands folded in her lap. She looked me straight in the face. 'Grace. Come on. Let's just talk about the elephant in the room. In the tent. The big rainbow elephant in the tent. It would be a relief to have to stop pretending I don't know, to be honest.'

I just looked at her. It wasn't that I didn't want her to know – I had a feeling she'd guessed a while ago – I just couldn't think of a single thing to say.

'So first, in Year Eight, every Food Tech class you make some excuse to stay behind and help Miss Perrin dry up the baking trays. Miss Perrin, also known as "Hot Miss Perrin" by everyone, including the teachers. Then, Year Nine . . . who was that sixth former who came in to help Reggie with his maths? Amanda? No idea how you got *any* maths done, the amount of time you spent gazing at her across the classroom.'

'Amelia,' I said. 'Not Amanda.'

Til raised her eyebrows and smirked. 'Well, of *course* you'd remember her name.'

I didn't reply. I just rolled my eyes.

'Year Ten,' she said, shuffling the cards absent-mindedly as she thought. 'Maybe that was a dry patch for you. Can't think of anyone. But this year, well, that one's easy. The girl from the library. That Welsh bird with the dimples. Sarah?'

I just shook my head and grinned. 'Shut up,' I said.

'It is Sarah though, isn't it?'

I half nodded, half shrugged. 'Think so, something like that.'

Til rolled her eyes. 'Like you haven't been writing her name all over the inside of your geography folder for the last four months.'

Til didn't say anything at all then, which turned out to be a good tactic because it made me want to say something.

'It was Elodie, in Year Ten.'

Til frowned for a second, thinking. 'The French exchange girl! But she was only here for a couple of weeks.'

'I know. Knew her for two weeks, thought about her for ten months.'

Til just smiled. 'The French, eh?' she said. 'Such heartbreakers.'

I just nodded and fiddled with my shoelace.

'Anyway!' Til said. 'Thank god that's out the way. Wasn't so hard, was it, you moron. Your turn to deal.'

And that was that, really. It was so typical of Til, to lure me into a momentous revelation then turn it into something totally mundane and run-of-the-mill that I ended up feeling like I'd just told her that my favourite pizza topping was sweetcorn. What kind of coming-out story was that to tell people?

We played for a bit longer without talking about anything very much. Then suddenly it occurred to me. 'Oh sorry, do you want to talk about you?'

'You what?'

'You know, do you want to talk about your feelings? Your family? About your mum being sick?'

'Shut up, Grace,' Til said, taking a swig of her beer.

'Right. OK. Sure.'

I knew Til would say that really. But it seemed rude not to offer.

Til's home never seemed a particularly happy one. It was just her and her mum in the little flat. Her mum had let Til have the only decent-sized bedroom so she slept on an inflatable mattress that had to be propped against the wall every morning so she could get in and out of the room. I'd met Til's mum plenty of times but heard her say only perhaps ten words. And mostly they were variations on 'I'm going to lie down'. She worked in the Post Office but she had a bad back, and 'bad nerves' as she called it, so was always phoning in sick. She left Til to do the shopping and the washing and to sort out the bills and to do most other things, it seemed.

Til didn't seem to talk to her mum very much, and she

never talked about her really, either. One Wednesday in Year Nine, Til had been nearly two hours late for school. When I'd asked her what had happened she just said, 'Mum . . . giving me grief again.'

I suppose I'd imagined the kind of grief my own mum would dish out – refusing to give me a lift, insisting I eat a bowl of cereal before leaving the house, unreasonable behaviour like that – although I did think that a two-hour delay seemed a little extreme. It wasn't until weeks later that Til let slip that the reason for her lateness that morning had been that her mum had decided, in a fit of paranoia, that the vents in the kitchen were leaking noxious fumes that were highly likely to kill both Til and herself in their sleep. To deal with this threat, she'd cut a bin liner into pieces, climbed up a stepladder and begun sealing the vents closed by covering them with plastic squares stuck down with duct tape. Halfway through her mission though, the ladder had toppled over, taking Til's mum with it, and she'd cracked her head open on the side of the worktop.

When Til had said she was late because her mum had been giving her grief, she meant the kind of grief that involved using an entire packet of toilet roll to clear up the litre of blood on the kitchen floor, riding in an ambulance and waiting in A&E while her mum had her head X-rayed.

'We should make a list,' I said after a while. 'Of all the stuff we're going to do this summer. You know, all the things we can do to live for the moment. All the ways we can seize the days. Carpe the diems.'

'Woah, woah, woah,' Til said, opening a new drink.

'What do you mean, "we"? This is your crusade, dude. Your mission. I just . . . go with the flow.'

'So do I!' I said. 'That's exactly what I do now. I just flow around, flowing with the flow. Flowing into whatever opportunities come my way.'

'Grace, you can't *plan* to go with the flow. That's too intense, man. If you're planning, that ain't flowing. That's swimming. That's like doing front crawl, you know?'

I pushed my hair out of my eyes. 'But, Til, I haven't got time to drift. I've got catching up to do. I've got to find things and do things and make things happen!'

Til laughed and shook her head. 'Whatever.'

She dealt the cards again.

Badger

The day after Til's birthday (part two) I took part in a choreographed dance routine.

In public.

On camera.

Dressed as a badger.

If that isn't evidence of how I had revolutionised my life, then I don't know what is.

I was walking through the station when I realised there seemed to be a lot of shouting and laughing going on, but then there was always a lot of noise in the station – charity choirs, people playing the free piano, steel drum bands, that kind of thing.

I had my earphones in so I wasn't paying too much attention until I almost walked right into them – a group of people, mostly looking slightly uncomfortable and bemused, pulling on a range of fancy dress costumes over their clothes. There was a man stepping into a Snow White dress so ornate that I wished Paddy had been there to see it. A woman was zipping up a giant bodysuit in the shape of a Galaxy Caramel. There were two men and two women in white jumpsuits and long wigs. I had no idea what they were supposed to be.

As I was staring at them, a man stepped into my path suddenly. He had curly hair and little round glasses. He smiled at me like he knew me. 'You'd like to earn ten pounds, wouldn't you?'

'Huh?' I said.

My instinct was to put my head down and walk quickly away. My instincts were shouting 'Avoid avoid avoid'. But I stopped myself, remembering that turning things down was no longer my default.

I took my earphones out.

'Do you want to earn ten pounds?' the guy said again. 'It'll only take five minutes.'

'What would I have to do?' I drew the line at immediately agreeing to anything. I may have been embracing life as a general principle, but I still had some standards regarding what (or who) I would embrace.

He didn't reply. He didn't reply in words, anyway. Instead he put both arms out in front of him, then crossed them across his chest. Then he put each one on each of his hips in turn.

I didn't need him to do any more.

'The Macarena?' I said.

The man stopped and his face broke into a wide smile. 'You know it!' he said. 'Even better.'

'I recognise it, definitely,' I said. I had watched my dad roll out the old Macarena routine at every wedding, family barbecue and Christmas drinks party I'd ever been to. He even did a low-energy version in the queue at Asda once, much to my dismay. That series of moves was burnt into my brain.

Still, it was a slightly bizarre request. 'But, like . . . why?'

'I'm proposing to my girlfriend. I didn't want to just go down the normal diamond-ring-in-the-chocolate-mousse route. I wanted to do something different. Bit more personal, you know. So the plan is basically this: everyone dresses up as all her favourite things and dances her favourite dance. Then I come out and pop the question.'

'Right, OK . . .' It all sounded most strange. 'Her favourite dance is really the Macarena?'

The bloke shrugged. 'Yeah. Why? What's your favourite dance?'

It was a good point. 'Don't suppose I've ever thought about it.'

'So anyway, if you can put this on, do the dance when the track starts, then that's it. I'll give you a tenner. Cash. Here and now.'

I found myself taking what he was holding out. A heavy piece of black and white fur. 'It's a badger suit,' he explained. 'She likes badgers.'

'Badgers?'

He nodded. 'Yep. As well as –' he gestured to the gang of slightly embarrassed-looking people giggling behind him – 'Disney princesses, chocolate and Abba.'

That explained the white jumpsuits, at least.

So there I was, holding a badger costume and agreeing to dance the Macarena in public. Even if I hadn't been embracing my new philosophy, I felt the conversation had already gone too far for me to back out. I had no choice but to step into the thick fur suit, pull on the enormous badger head and join the others, wondering how on earth we'd ended up here when we were just going about our business one quiet Sunday morning.

'OK, team!' Romeo said, clapping his hands. 'Her train gets in at eight minutes past. When I see her come towards the barriers, I'll start the music. When she sees me, I'll turn it down so I can do the whole one-knee thing. So basically, just dance till the music stops!'

At least, I thought, as I loitered around with the other recruits, at least no one can see my face.

When the music started, I flung my arms out in front of me, trying to keep in sync with the others as much as I could, bearing in mind how hard it was to see them through my tiny badger eye-holes.

Once I got going, I had the weirdest feeling that I might actually be enjoying myself. I had no idea when I'd left home to buy a lightbulb and some face wipes that an hour later I'd be dancing the Macarena in a full badger suit as the 11.08 from London pulled into platform five.

But then, as the passengers climbed off the train and started to swarm towards the barrier, something funny happened to the music. I think the CD must've started skipping in the little stereo the guy had brought with him because the same three or four seconds kept repeating again and again.

Now let me ask you: what would you do if you were

performing a dance routine and the same snippet of music kept repeating? Would you:

Ignore the music and continue to work through the steps of the whole routine undeterred?

OR

Repeat the snippet of dance routine that matched the snippet of music, and hope to get back on track when the music did?

It's not an easy predicament to find oneself in, but I plumped for B.

Unfortunately, the moment the music decided to stick was the part of the routine where you're supposed to slap yourself on the hips with each hand in turn.

So there I was, standing in the middle of Brighton station in a badger suit, repeatedly slapping myself on the bum.

I have a feeling it wasn't quite the romantic spectacle the Romeo man was going for because I suddenly felt him pulling on my arm, 'Stop it!' he hissed. 'What are you doing?' The interruption threw me completely, so I just stopped altogether.

Anyway, the lady in question finally arrived and seemed more than a little alarmed by the spectacle of the bizarrely dressed strangers circling her boyfriend, who by this point was down on one knee.

I wasn't close enough to hear what was said, but the woman didn't look very happy, and shortly after, neither did the man. She stormed off in the direction of the station exit and he jogged after her.

'She said no!' I heard someone say.

Then the Snow White man called, 'She said no, everyone! It's all off! Abort! Abort!'

The whole scene seemed to have got a little out of hand so I quickly slipped off the badger suit, draped it over a railing and made my exit.

On the way home, I typed a tweet:

Just dressed up as a badger and slapped my own bum at the station. #youonlyliveonce

The Greatest of Ease

I was surprised to find that my badger bum tweet had proved rather popular. It had been retweeted thirty-five times and people were even sharing their own stories with my #youonlyliveonce hashtag.

All in all, I was pretty pleased with my progress. First the donkey ride, then Til's birthday – including the unplanned and understated coming out episode – and then the slapping of the badger bum. So far, so carpe diem.

I felt I wanted to do something more though. I wanted to up the ante. I wanted to do something that I categorically would not have even considered if it hadn't been for my new philosophy.

I went back to the 'My Ultimate Bucket List' website and scanned down. I'd seen this one before, but this time I paused on it:

Do a bungee jump

It was the classic stunt, wasn't it?

It was basically the poster child for the whole concept of living for the moment. When you saw photos of people online who were fun and free and happy and embracing life, they were invariably dangling upside down over some beautiful waterfall with a strap around their ankles, their hands in the air and a beaming smile on their face.

I couldn't even think where one might go to take part in a bungee jump. I was obviously keen that it should be a reputable arrangement. I may have become wild these days, but I wasn't about to be throwing myself head-first off some unofficial crane with a dressing gown cord tied around my legs.

I heard Ollie's bedroom door open. It was one in the afternoon so about the usual time he made an appearance.

Ollie was taking a year out after finishing college to work out what he was going to do next. The only thing was, his year out was fast becoming two years and I don't think he was any nearer to making a plan. He said he wanted to find his 'passion' but so far the only places he'd tried looking were in his bed, in his PlayStation controller and in the pub at the bottom of the hill.

'Ollie!' I called. 'Come here a minute.'

'What?' he grunted, appearing in my doorway in his filthy pyjama bottoms and no top. He hadn't shaved for a while but he wasn't really hairy enough for a proper beard so he just looked like he had a bit of a grubby face.

'If one wanted to take part in a bungee-jump type activity, where would one go?'

He crossed his arms over his chest. 'One?' He raised an eyebrow. 'Why are you talking like a weirdo?'

'OK, me,' I said.

'Ha. You. As if.'

I ignored him. I could hardly object to this response when I'd spent the last sixteen years avoiding anything with any element of risk. Avoiding anything that didn't directly contribute to my ultimate goal of academic success.

'Marvin did a bungee jump, didn't he? For his eighteenth?' Marvin was Ollie's best friend. He was just the type of person to do a bungee jump. He was currently travelling around India on his own. Last week he uploaded a photo of himself squatting in the street next to an elderly bearded gentleman cooking something in a pan on an open fire. In fact, I thought, Marvin could be another idol for me. I decided to consider this later.

Ollie narrowed his eyes, thinking for a moment. 'Sort of. It wasn't a bungee cord though . . . more of a swing. They wrap a thing around your waist, crank you up to the top of a metal arch, then let you go. And *whoosh!*' He made a swooping motion with his arm. 'You swing right down.'

I thought about this. 'Is it high?'

Ollie nodded. 'Seventy metres or so, I think.'

I still wasn't sure if it counted though. I mean, a bungee jump was iconic, wasn't it? You could say to people, 'I've done a bungee jump,' and sound impressive and daredevil and wild. I wasn't sure 'I went on a sort of massive swing thing' had the same ring to it.

'It looked amazing, actually,' Ollie said. 'Because you've got the strap around your middle, and you're going horizontal as well as down, so it looks like you're actually flying. For a minute, anyway.'

Flying. This was more like it, I suppose. Imagine feeling

like you're flying! This was the kind of mind-blowing once in a lifetime sensation I was after.

What did you do this morning, Grace?'

Oh, you know, a bit of a flying through the air with the greatest of ease.

Ollie looked at me. He could tell I was seriously considering it. 'There is no *way* you're going to do that,' he said, pushing his hands in his pyjama pockets and yawning. 'No way.'

'You don't know that. I might do.'

'If you do that I will personally give you fifty pounds.'

'Fine,' I said, turning back round to face my computer. 'We'll see.'

The fact that Ollie seemed to find the idea of me doing anything daring so hard to believe made my mind up.

Rush

It was called Rush.

I realised I'd seen the huge steel arc hundreds of times when I've been on the bus along the seafront but I'd never really thought about what it was. Up close, it was enormous. A dirty, dark, industrial-looking metal structure with a platform near the top, and some kind of rope hanging from the peak. It was rather intimidating, as a spectacle.

There was a small prefab hut at the bottom, a bit like one of the mobile classrooms at school. Above it was a sign painted on a wooden board. 'Rush: Don't look down', it said. Where exactly you were supposed to look, I wasn't sure.

I went into the hut. There was a man on reception in a T-shirt with the same Rush logo as the sign. He had a beard and his hair scraped up into a sort of top-knot.

'Howdy,' he said with a smile.

'Hello,' I said. 'Can I have a go? On the swing thing?'

The man laughed. 'Swing thing! It's seventy metres in the air, it's not a kiddies' play park!'

'Yes, I know, sorry.' I felt my cheeks flush. I hadn't meant to insult the extremeness of the extreme sport.

'We've got a slot at three o'clock if you can hang on a bit?'

I said I could and the man gave me a clipboard with a form to fill in asking me to confirm I didn't have back or heart problems, and that I wasn't pregnant. The entire second page of the form seemed to be a very long-winded and formal statement that could be essentially summed up as, 'If you die, it's not our fault.' This made me slightly nervous to say the least.

'It is safe, isn't it?' I called to the man from my plastic chair in the hut. 'I mean, I get that it's meant to be a bit scary but there's no actual danger involved, is there?'

The man shrugged. 'Nothing in life is one hundred per cent guaranteed safe. You could walk out of here and be hit by a bus. A bus could plunge down off the main road and flatten this whole hut. Everything's dangerous, isn't it, in the end. And not just buses.'

'Right,' I said, looking down at the form, looking at the **bold** lettering across the top:

AT PARTICIPANT'S OWN RISK.

'Why do you want to do it, anyway?' the man asked, lazily flicking the elastic band on his wrist. 'You don't look the type, to be honest.'

I looked down at myself. I looked quite normal, I thought. T-shirt. Trainers. I didn't think there was anything about me to say whether I was or wasn't the type to enjoy a go on a giant swing.

'What do you mean?' I demanded.

He shrugged. 'Oh, I dunno really. Just seem a bit uptight.'

The cheek of it!

I frowned.

'No?' he said. 'Well, obviously not, as you're here. What is it that appeals?'

Looking up at the daunting steel structure with the waist strap flapping loosely in the wind, it was quite a difficult question to answer, it had to be said.

'I'm living every moment as if it were my last,' I told him.

He laughed. 'Fair enough. Hope it isn't your last, then!'

He laughed again. I did not.

'Joke!' he said. 'You'll be fine.'

I decided to take the precaution of getting a photo of the Rush sign and slogan and posting it on Twitter, Snapchat and Instagram so that if I didn't make it off the swing alive, at least people would know how daring and adventurous I'd been.

Three people liked it immediately, and someone called Dolly Rocket replied:

Been meaning to do that for months, but just know I couldn't handle it!

The man with the top-knot had to stay and man reception, so my assistant for the feat itself was a boy called Saul, who seemed a bit young to be entrusted with safely stringing me up from a giant metal arch.

'I'm eighteen,' he said when I enquired.

'Are you properly trained?'

He shrugged. 'Not much to it, really. Just strap you in, undo the clip and you're away.'

'Right,' I said. I was beginning to have serious doubts.

I followed Saul up fifteen flights of corrugated metal steps. They had a handrail but they were swaying gently in the wind and I must say the whole set-up had a rather temporary, unstable feel about it.

I started to think how I could get out of it. I so badly wanted to be able to tell people I'd done it but if I was lying dead at the bottom I wouldn't be telling anyone anything. I started to think: I could just make it up, couldn't I? I could imagine what it would feel like to be swung from a great height and just say that. Make up a bit of stuff about the rush of the wind and feeling so alive.

'Did you want pictures?' Saul asked as we reached the top, me red faced and panting, him barely breaking a sweat.

'Pictures?'

'There's a camera,' he said, pointing to a black box on a stem in front of us. 'It's automatic. Gets a great shot of you mid-flight.'

Too right I wanted pictures. If I was going to go through this, I wanted all the photographic evidence available. I'd realised I'd started to think of things a bit like that tree in the forest that people talk about: 'If a tree falls in a forest, and no one was there to see it, did it really fall at all?'

If I didn't share hard evidence of what I was doing, did it even count as doing it? What was the point if no one knew?

Say Cheese

Learning of the camera had given me a renewed enthusiasm for the endeavour.

Saul pulled the thick padded strap around my waist and pulled it tight. Ollie had given me a rundown of what to expect and warned me that I should wear soft, loose clothes if I didn't want to end up with the button of my jeans embedded somewhere in my small intestine. With this in mind, I'd borrowed a pair of Ollie's old joggers as my outfit for the occasion. I'd had to hitch them up at least eight times on the walk up the steps but now I could see that I was right to have chosen them.

With my harness on, I was ready to go.

I stood at the platform and looked down (contrary to the slogan's instruction). I can't say I'd ever had a genuine phobia of heights, but I did have a healthy anxiety about anything that could lead to an immediate and grisly death, and it seemed to me that balancing precariously on a wooden platform seventy metres in the air with nothing but a strap of fabric to support you fell quite firmly into that category.

'So, what now?' I asked Saul. 'Do I just – WOAH WAIT!'

I'd been thinking I'd have a moment to compose myself, to take in the view, to think some big thoughts about life and the world, and then, when I was good and ready, leap gracefully into my flight. But suddenly I was being hoisted upwards by the cord attached to my waist strap. I was dangling a few feet above the platform, my arms and legs hanging loosely. I felt like a beetle being plucked out of the ground by a sadistic child, keen to watch its legs flail about in panic.

'OK, ready?' Saul said. 'Remember to smile for the camera!'

'OK but wait, I –'

But Saul didn't wait. He reached up and released some kind of catch above my back and then

OH

MY

GOD.

The absolute speed of the thing! It was like I was just falling from space. Which I was, in a way. As I was careering towards the ground, I honestly thought the cord was too long and nothing was going to stop me smashing into the concrete below.

But then the whole swing dynamic kicked in. I was no longer falling downwards but swinging forwards. This, I realised, was the flight element. This is what I was here for.

I became aware of some flashing in front of me. The camera! Somehow, through my absolute terror, I had to remain focused on my goal: to obtain photographic evidence of me doing something daring and exciting, and looking exhilarated yet elegant while doing it. I stretched my arms out either side of me, imaging myself as graceful as a swallow in flight.

More flashes. How many photos was it taking?

As the swing reached its climax I had two horrible realisations:

1) I was now almost as high in the air as I'd been when I'd been dropped from the platform. I'd swung down and all the way up the other side. Which meant, now, I had to fall all the way back down again. And backwards! Would this horror never end?

2) My legs were suspiciously cold.

Despite the extreme G-forces being exerted on my head I managed to peer down and my worst fears were confirmed. The comfortable, loose elastic of Ollie's joggers had let me down. My trousers were around my ankles.

There was very little I could do. I was at the mercy of gravity. I wriggled around a bit and tried to reach them but there was no way it was going to happen. I just had to ride it out. Each climb and fall seemed to go on forever.

Finally, the swing started to slow. I was near the ground again, and Saul was approaching, ambling towards me from the direction of the hut.

I was still suspended in mid-air a few feet above the ground. I was floating around Saul's chest height. My trousers were still around my ankles. I was, apart from my grey M&S pants, naked from the waist down. It was less than ideal.

'Enjoy that?' Saul asked, trying to lower me to the ground.

'Sort of,' I said, wriggling my legs to try to find the floor with my feet. 'Bit of a wardrobe malfunction!' I thought it was better to make a joke of it than pretend it wasn't happening. Saul obviously thought otherwise though as he didn't reply, or even smile, keeping his eyes firmly on the top half of my body as he positioned me upright and released the strap.

I don't know if it was the sudden release from my support strap or having my trousers pinning my ankles together, but as Saul unclipped me, I staggered unsteadily for a moment, then fell to my knees.

'Argh!' I said. 'God. Feel all funny.'

Saul smiled shyly, but he was clearly still unsure where to look. I stayed sitting on the floor as I finally managed to wrestle my bum back into my trousers. I sat there, breathing hard. Saul was obviously relieved to be able to look at me again.

'Bit of a wobbly flight!' he said brightly as we made our way to the hut. 'Most people don't wriggle around so much!'

'I know,' I said. 'I was just trying to . . .' I stopped myself. I decided not to bring up the issue of the missing trousers again.

Top-knot guy was sitting on his stool at reception, flicking through a newspaper.

'You've landed!' he said as I stumbled in, still unsteady as my body readjusted to being on solid ground. 'Have fun?'

'Sort of.'

'Let's take a look at the evidence then.' He turned a computer screen on his desk around to face me and flicked through the images. There were three in total – I guess the machine didn't save all of them.

Every one was a complete disaster.

Exhibit one: me, my eyes squeezed shut, a long trail of dribble stretching from my chin to my chest.

Exhibit two: my arms outstretched but my head angled down, horror on my face as I realise that I'm no longer completely dressed.

Exhibit three: a full-on bum shot. Where I'd been desperately trying to retrieve my errant joggers I'd somehow spun myself round so that all you could see were my pants, my – still quite yellow – lumpy legs and my feet flailing about at the bottom.

Saul and top-knot guy eyed the images with interest.

'Number two is sort of OK?' Saul suggested.

I sighed. 'It's the best we've got.'

I didn't exactly have much choice. There was no way I was going away without photographic evidence of the trauma I'd just been through. There was also no way I was going through the trauma again in order to obtain a more attractive shot.

I paid my money, the top-knot guy printed out my photo and slipped it into a cardboard envelope, and I left.

While I'd been in the air more people had replied to my photo of the Rush sign. To my surprise, there were several people questioning whether I'd actually go through with it.

Pics or it didn't happen!

said a girl from my French class.

Such a liar

said Til.

Til! Even Til was trolling me now.

There was no way I was going through what I'd just been through only to have people doubting my daring. Pride about my attitude overrode vanity about my looks. I slipped the official swing photo out of the cardboard envelope and laid it on the ground. I took a photo of it with my phone, and uploaded it to Twitter and Instagram with the caption:

I looked down! #mistake #yolo

The likes and replies rolled in at once, and I walked home on a high, surprised and pleased, both with my own courage, and with the public approval of it.

Ollie

When I got home, I found Ollie in the kitchen, eating Coco Pops out of a mixing bowl and smiling a wide, unnatural smile. His face was frozen in the position, like the Joker from *Batman*. It was most unnerving.

'What's wrong with your face?' I said.

His expression remained unchanged.

'I'm smiling.'

'Well, quite. Why?'

'It's been scientifically proven,' he said, his stretched cheeks making his voice sound like a ventriloquist's, 'that if you smile, you automatically feel happier. The very act of smiling releases a chemical from your brain and, boom, you're happy.'

'Is it working?'

His smile fell. 'Nope.' He sighed. 'Anyway, you all right?'

'I did it,' I said proudly.

'What?'

'I flew!'

It took him a moment to realise what I was talking about.

'You – what? You didn't? Rush?'

I nodded.

He narrowed his eyes. 'Nah. No way. You wouldn't. It's well sketchy down there. It's all run by kids and the ropes look like they were picked up off the beach. I know you. You would've taken one look and been like, "I'm sorry but I'm not sure all health and safety legislation has been properly adhered to on these premises."'

I shook my head. 'Nope. It *was* sketchy, but I did it anyway. Because that's what I'm like now, Ollie. Risky. Edgy.'

Ollie finished his Coco Pops and took his bowl over to the sink. He sat back down at the table. 'Yeah?' he grinned. 'Prove it.'

I thrust the photograph towards him. He tipped it out of the envelope and held it out in front of him.

'Ha! No way!'

I nodded once, and crossed my arms. 'See.'

'But, Gracie, what has *happened* here?' He peered more closely at the photo. 'Why are you . . . ? Is that your . . . ? Where are your trousers? Or *my* trousers, I should say.'

I took the photo back from him. 'They didn't exactly fit, did they. On account of your ginormous bum. So it didn't end so well.'

'Ha!' Ollie shook his head and grinned. 'Amazing. A. Maze. Ing.'

'It was good actually,' I told him. 'Properly like flying.'

'Can't believe you actually did it! What's got into you lately, baby sis? You going crazy now your exams are over? Didn't know you had it in you.'

I shrugged and took an apple out of the fruit bowl. Then I put it back and took a Toffee Crisp out of the cupboard because I was young and I was only going to live once.

'Just want to make the most of things,' I said as I ripped off the orange wrapper. 'I don't want to be lying on my death bed and the only excitement I have to look back on is opening a new packet of Post-its. You owe me fifty quid, by the way.'

Ollie waved the suggestion away. We both knew he'd struggle to find fifty pence, much less fifty pounds. He yawned and rubbed the back of his head. 'You're right, you know. There's something in all this. Who knows what I'm going to have to look back on.'

'What are you going to do, though?' I said, picking toffee out of my teeth. 'Your year out is turning into a decade out. It'll turn into a life out if you're not careful.'

Ollie smiled but his eyes looked sad. 'I know,' he said. 'Tell me about it.'

But actually it was him who told me about it.

He just started talking. Telling me all kinds of things. Like how he thought something would come to him if he just relaxed and waited – his calling would call – but how he was starting to think there was nothing he would ever actually enjoy doing. He said that he thought he would get into computers but his maths A-level grade had been too low for him to think that a possibility any more. He even told me about a girl who he'd been seeing but had got frustrated with him never having any money – or any enthusiasm – for anything.

'Have you ever noticed how everyone's got a thing

these days?'

'How do you mean?' I said. 'What thing?

'OK, so look at this.' He took his phone out of his pocket and opened Twitter. 'Look at everyone's profiles.' He started to read some aloud. '"Passionate about fitness, healthy eating and well-being", "Artist, illustrator and comic book connoisseur", "Traveller. Wanderer. Environmental campaigner". See? Everyone's got a thing. A brand. A *calling*.'

'Being a traveller isn't a calling. It's just going on holiday.'

He ignored me. 'Even you, you've got a thing. You've got your study and your books and your ten thousand A grades.'

'Great,' I said, chewing. 'That's just great. My personal brand is being square and boring.'

'Yeah, but you've got something,' Ollie insisted. 'That's the whole point. I haven't got anything. I was OK at school – not that clever, not that cool. I've done some pointless jobs that I was OK at, but that I didn't love. I like watching TV and playing PlayStation and listening to music but so what? Who *am* I, Grace?'

Post

I didn't say anything. I was too busy trying to work out how I could shed my own personal brand of tedium and safety and prudence, how I could disassociate myself from *that* and show people I was now *this*. Fun and brave and cool. I had rebranded. I was different now.

Ollie sighed. 'Ha. Sorry, sis. Bit of gut spillage there,' he seemed embarrassed suddenly.

'No. It's fine,' I said. 'I don't know who you are, though. Sorry. You're just Ollie.'

He nodded sadly.

'Anyway, you keep going,' he said, standing up and taking an apple from the bowl. 'You've got the right idea, I reckon.'

He traipsed off back up to his bedroom and I sat at the table rolling my Toffee Crisp wrapper into a ball and thinking about how Ollie had just said more to me in the last fifteen minutes than he had in the last two years and that I was pretty sure that this was a direct result of Operation Seize the Day.

It was interesting, I thought to myself, all this talking that was happening now I was doing things. I thought I was just going to get a few snaps of me looking carefree on horseback, but now here I was, having heart-to-hearts. First Til in the tent and now Ollie. I quite liked it, I decided.

I was still sitting at the table when Mum came in from work.

'Post for you,' she said, sliding a postcard across the table to me. It showed a picture of the Eiffel Tower. I knew who it would be from.

Nan often sent Ollie and me postcards featuring images from all around the world. She never went to the places – she never went anywhere as I far as I could tell – but she liked to pick up postcards from shops and send us random little notes. I turned the card over.

Dear Grace,
Nan here. I knew a French man once. Pierre, his name was. Well, actually I don't think that was his name. That's just what your grandfather called him because he was French. Handsome. He used to deliver meat from a van. One morning he asked me if I'd like to kiss him after he'd handed me a packet of rindless bacon. I said no.
I've never been to Paris. Always wanted to go but too late now I'm old.
Come and see me if you like.
  Love Nan

She always said that. 'Come and see me if you like.' Like she wasn't bothered either way. It was curious, I thought. Your own grandmother playing hard to get.

'What did she have to say, then?' Mum asked and I passed her the card.

'You should go and see her,' Mum said. 'I know she's difficult but she is your nan. It would mean a lot to Dad if you made the effort.'

I was about to make some kind of non-committal yeah-maybe-soon kind of noise when it suddenly occurred to me. I'm not supposed to be in the business of turning things down. Fobbing people off, making excuses, putting things off till later. That kind of thing was for the old Grace. That wasn't me any more.

Maybe I would go and see Nan, I thought. I'd get on a train and buy a bunch of flowers and just GO.

And then, as I was having that idea, a more exciting one started to form.

I reached for my phone, scrolled down to Til's name and pressed the call button.

'Yeah?'

'Til, do you want to come to Paris with me?'

PART 3

During which I visit the City of Light and my grandmother becomes an unwitting internet sensation

Mini-Break

'You lezzing on to me?'

'What?'

'Are you asking me on a romantic mini-break with you? Because I ain't into that, I told you. Also, not being funny, Gracie, but you need to learn to play it cool. I know you're new to this but you don't *open* with an invitation to Paris. Like, woah, too much, you know?'

'Do shut up, Til,' I said. 'I'm serious. Do you want to come to Paris? With me. And my nan.'

'Your nan?'

'Yeah. She's always wanted to go. I want to take her. But she can be a bit . . . much so I need someone to come with me. I'll pay.' Actually, Dad said he would, but it was all the same to Til.

That got her interested. 'Tell me more.'

'That's as far as I've got really. But basically, we go to Paris with my nan and give her the trip of a lifetime, while at the same time seeing one of the most amazing cities in the world and having a memorable and all-round spectacular time ourselves.'

I heard Til open a packet of crisps. 'Sure,' she said, her mouth full. 'Why not?'

Three days later, Til, Nan and I were at St Pancras International station.

Despite claiming she'd always wanted to go, Nan hadn't seemed particularly enthusiastic when I'd phoned to invite her on her trip of a lifetime.

'Paris?' she said. 'Abroad?'

'Yes,' I said. 'France.'

'I shan't go on a plane. They're more than likely to crash, you know.'

I decided not to get into the statistical analysis of this point. 'We can go on the train.'

'I don't need taking out on a day trip, you know, Grace. I know you kids don't really want to be spending time with your boring nan. I might be old but I'm not a charity case.'

I'd been so excited about the spontaneity of whisking my grandmother away to Paris at a moment's notice that it hadn't occurred to me for a minute that she might resist.

'I'm not doing it out of charity, Nan!' I protested. 'Basically, what it is,' I lied, 'is that I really want to go but Mum won't let me go on my own, and her and Dad are too busy with work and Paddy and everything so I wondered if you would come with me?'

Nan sighed. 'Oh, I suppose so. Not for too long though, mind.'

Nan was understandably surprised by the imminence of my suggested travel date but she nonetheless agreed. 'I suppose I'm not getting any younger.'

During the flurry of organisational activity in the couple of days running up to the trip, I'd completely forgotten to mention to Nan that Til was coming too.

'Who's this one?' Nan said, turning around from the passenger seat of Dad's car as he drove us to the station.

'Oh yeah, sorry. This is Til, Nan. My friend. She's coming with us.'

'Hi,' Til said.

Nan looked at Til like she was finding her a bit confusing. 'Til?' she said slowly and carefully. 'Til? Like a cash register?'

'Like Matilda, Nan,' I said. I eyed Til carefully for signs of offence, but she just raised her eyebrows in a vaguely amused expression.

I found being at the station moderately stressful because I was both trying to deal with the paperwork and luggage aspect, as well as making sure Nan didn't say anything inappropriate to Til, or anyone else.

It had been quite some years since Nan had ventured abroad and either things were different back then, or else she'd just forgotten the various administrative and security procedures, because she seemed most exasperated by 'all the stupid hoops we have to jump through'. By this she meant showing our tickets (once) and our passports (also once).

'Anything else you need to see?' she asked the nervous-looking French man at passport control. 'My birth certificate? My medical records? My bra?'

The man just nervously shook his head and I ushered Nan through. Unfortunately, her thick metal bracelets set the metal detector off and the female security officer indicated that she should step aside for a pat-down. Nan made a huge fuss the whole way through, including loudly announcing that if she was going to get felt up in public then they could at least let her have the 'dusky French fella'.

As we stood on the platform with our bags, waiting for the doors of the Eurostar train to open, I took my phone out of my pocket. 'Let's have a photo then, Nan!' I said, holding it up.

I thought she'd refuse or at least grumble some objections, but to my surprise, Nan leant on her suitcase with one hand, and spread the other arm out to gesture to the huge Eurostar logo on the train behind her, and smiled widely.

'Excellent,' I said, laughing.

'I'm posting that,' I said to Til.

I added it to Instagram and Twitter with the hashtag:

#NanOnTour

Nan's photo seemed to go down quite well with my 234 followers, as within fifteen minutes or so, fourteen people had either liked it or posted a comment.

'Look, Nan,' I said, showing the screen. 'People like your photo.'

'What's that?' Nan said, squinting at the screen. 'Who does?'

'Oh, just people,' I said. 'Some of them I know. Some of them I don't. But they click on this little button if they like something, and that's what they've done.'

Nan peered at the screen for a bit longer, still seeming confused.

Then suddenly she broke into a wide smile. 'Well, we ought to give them some more then! Here.' She took the Eurostar in-journey menu out of the pocket in the back of the seat in front and held it up next to her face. 'Go on! Take another!' She grinned manically.

'Oh, OK,' I said, opening my phone's camera. 'OK.'

'You're going to put it up, are you?' Nan asked, anxiously peering over my shoulder. 'So people can press the button to say they like it?'

'Uh, yeah, sure,' I said. I posted this one to Instagram too, again with the #NanOnTour hashtag.

Out of the corner of my eye, I caught Til turning away to the window to hide her smile.

Nan made me take three or four more photos of her in various poses in her seat, but I had to lie about posting them online. There were only so many photos of my grandmother on public transport that people needed to see.

'How many people have liked them now?' Nan would ask every so often.

'Fifty-eight,' I'd lie. 'Sixty, now.'

'Sixty!' Nan chuckled to herself. 'Well, I never.'

After half an hour or so Nan nodded off, and I was given a break from my role as official mini-break photographer.

'Sorry about my nan,' I said to Til. Although I was glad to have someone with me, I was now starting to wish I'd asked Ollie to come instead. Someone who knew Nan like I did.

Til just shrugged. 'She's fine. Don't worry about it.'

'I know she can be weird.'

'Grace, man. My mum once made me come home from school because a seagull had been on the window sill too long and she was worried it was really a spy camera sent by the government to stop her benefits. I know what a difficult family is and yours ain't it.'

'OK,' I said. 'Funny though, isn't it? Who knew Nan would turn out to be such a social media addict?'

Nan slept for about half of the two and a half hours it took for our train to make its way onto the continent. She spent the other half of the journey talking about people she knew from her road, from the post office, from the pub on the corner, jumping from one to the other without pausing for breath:

'And you know Pauline's granddaughter is pregnant, of course. And Pauline says to me the other day, "They've chosen a name for the baby. It's a girl and they're going to call it Lavender. Pretty, isn't it?" And I says, "Well yes, Pauline, but what are they going to call it for short? Lav?" Little baby Lav! Can you imagine?'

'And Margaret was telling me how she went to the funeral of some old boy from the day centre, and one of the blokes in the audience had on a musical tie! I ask you! Why would you wear a musical tie to a funeral! The son's in the middle of reading the eulogy and you've got Rudolph the flippin' Red Nosed Reindeer playing at the back of the church!'

As we pulled into Paris Gare du Nord, Nan seemed to get quiet. It was almost as if she was nervous, the way she blinked slightly as the platforms came into view.

106

'We're here then, are we?' she said.

'Yep. Welcome to Paris, Nan,' I said smiling, as if I was any more an expert on the city than she was.

'Yes, quite,' Nan muttered. She got unsteadily to her feet and smoothed her skirt down. 'Let's get on with it, then.'

Nan on Tour

As we walked down the platform and through the station, Nan was quiet and I wondered if it was all a bit much for her. She seemed to rally though when she spotted the heavily armed French soldiers patrolling the station.

'Oh, I've got to have a photo with one of them,' she said, abandoning her bag with Til and approaching the man. 'Photo!' she called, miming a camera action. 'Photo!'

The soldier didn't smile. Instead he shook his head sharply and said, 'No photo,' and strode on.

'Miserable git,' Nan mumbled. 'Here, let's do it on the sly, Grace. You ready? Quick!'

Nan positioned herself just in front of a soldier who had his back turned. She held her arms up, as if holding her own invisible gun and smiled.

I dutifully took the picture and this time, I did upload it. It was kind of funny. Once again, the internet agreed and this time I could impress Nan with the genuine number of likes and replies she picked up.

'How funny,' Nan chuckled to herself. 'Funny old world.'

We headed out of the station and joined the back of the taxi queue.

'You're wearing man's shoes,' Nan said to Til as we waited.

'Nan!' I said, alarmed. 'She's not.'

'I am actually,' Til said, leaning against the railings and lifting up one of her heavy black lace-up boots to admire it. 'Way more comfortable.'

Nan nodded once. 'Very good,' she said. 'Very sensible. I can't bear it when girls wear those ridiculous stilettos. What if you needed to outrun a predator? Wouldn't stand a chance.'

I had the name of our hotel, our booking reference and a small map of the area printed off and tucked in my bag so when the taxi driver asked where we were going I was prepared, which was lucky as he didn't speak any English.

I sat in the front and he seemed keen to chat. If this had been before my French GCSE oral, I would have been either delighted at this opportunity for authentic practice, or aghast at how little I understood. As it was, I just felt slightly embarrassed at the number of times I had to say '*Je ne comprends pas*' while the driver just smiled and shook his head as if to say 'Never mind'.

Nan seemed keen to get in on the chat, insisting on loudly repeating the two French phrases she knew from the back seat any time there was a lull in conversation.

'*Je ne regrette rien.*'

and

'*Voulez-vous coucher avec moi?*'

The taxi driver's only response to these interjections was to smile shyly and continue trying to talk to me, but even if my French listening skills had been more polished, I still would've found it difficult to maintain a serious conversation about French transport infrastructure with my grandmother poking her head through the gap in the seats every five minutes to proposition the taxi driver in heavily accented French.

We checked into our hotel, which was called Maison Vert and was on the border of the eighteenth and ninth *arrondisements* in an area called Pigalle. On the same road were several shops with mannequins dressed in lacy underwear in the window beneath neon signs that said things like 'Scarlet's' and 'Fantasy'. One place cut to the chase and just had 'SEX' in metre-high letters above the door.

Nan stood on the edge of the pavement and looked around her.

'Grace, why have you brought me to a red-light district?'

'I haven't!' I protested, although I had to agree the evidence suggested otherwise. 'It's the perfect location to explore all the key landmarks. It'll be fine, I'm sure.'

'Well, I shan't be standing too long at any corners, I can tell you,' Nan said, peering closely at a mannequin's nipple tassels. 'I get enough offers when I'm down The Crown at home. Can do without the French starting on at me too.'

I had a detailed itinerary written out in pencil in the back of a notebook, complete with addresses, opening times, prices and directions. It was a perfect blueprint for the quintessential Parisian weekend.

Til saw me studying it and peered over my shoulder. 'Still going with the flow then, is it?'

I didn't look up. 'We've been through this. I'm on an accelerated flow path. To ensure maximum flow at all times, I have to put careful plans in place.'

'Right,' Til said, fanning herself with a leaflet. 'Well, what does the masterplan say we're doing for dinner? I'm starving.'

Dogs Cats Zebra

The plan said we were going to Les Trois Canards, which was, according to the guidebook, 'a traditional French bistro oozing with classic Parisian charm'.

The restaurant did indeed look exactly as you'd imagine a traditional French restaurant should look – white tablecloths, little jars of red wine and heavy velvet curtains everywhere, as well as waiters who looked both elegant and a little bit miffed.

The menu was leather-bound and printed in curling italics on thick yellow paper. All in French of course. As it should be! And I was confident that with five years of French study under my belt I should be more than capable of something as rudimentary as translating a menu.

I was wrong.

'Well, it's all in foreign,' Nan said, closing it immediately. 'I might as well close my eyes and point at anything. I want egg and chips. I'll have egg and chips, please, waiter!' she called.

'Nan, no!' I said feeling myself blush. 'You can't have egg and chips. It's a waste.' I opened her menu back up. 'Here,

112

look. *Steak tartare*. You like steak.'

Nan looked suspiciously at where I was pointing. 'OK fine. I'll have it well done. With plenty of ketchup.'

The waiter barely moved his face while taking our order so I had no idea what he made of my French – if he understood, if he didn't, or if he was just doing an unflattering sketch of us all as he scratched his pencil on his notepad. We'd just have to wait and see.

He returned fifteen minutes later and put the plate down in front of Nan.

'Ugh!' She recoiled in horror. 'What is *that*!' She put her napkin up to her mouth, as if she was concerned her plate may be emitting noxious fumes.

The waiter raised a weary eyebrow. '*Steak tartare, madame.*'

'Grace!' Nan said turning to me. 'There's been a horrible mistake! They haven't cooked it! They're trying to kill me!'

Til and I looked at Nan's plate. It was a ball of raw mince, topped with a raw egg. It did indeed seem that there had been some mistake.

'*Excusez-moi*,' I called, as the waiter was already turning away from us. '*Il y a une problème. Je pense que* you have forgotten to cook *le steak*?'

'*Non*,' he said sharply. '*C'est steak tartare.*'

I looked at Til and she looked at me and then she got her phone out.

'Ah yeah,' she said after a minute. 'It says this on Wikipedia: "Steak tartare is a meat dish made from minced raw beef or –" OH GOD NO.'

113

Nan and I both jumped. 'What?'

' "... or horsemeat", ' Til finished. 'Oh, my actual good god.'

Nan jolted her chair backwards and sat, as if pinned to the back of it, staring at her plate in horror. 'It's a horse!' she cried.

I had a feeling I was losing control of the situation. 'I'm sure it's not . . .' I looked around for the waiter. '*Excusez-moi? Le steak* is *boeuf, oui? Ce n'est pas une* horse?'

But everyone ignored me. And Nan had had enough anyway. She was getting to her feet, pulling on her coat and making for the door. I threw a small wad of Euros on the table and Til and I trailed after her.

Outside, an American couple were perusing the menu in the window.

'You don't want to go in there!' Nan said to their surprised faces. 'They're serving all sorts and calling it dinner! Tried to give me a horse! And they didn't even cook it. They've got it all, back there, I shouldn't wonder. Dogs. Cats. Zebra! They think just because you're foreign you'll just take what you're given and not say a word. Well, not I! I won't have it.'

We eventually found a pizza takeaway place a few roads away. Nan told the man behind the counter all about our raw horse fiasco while he prepared us two large ham and pineapple pizzas and tried not to laugh.

We ate the pizza sitting on plastic chairs on the pavement. It wasn't the Parisian dinner I had pictured, and I told Til as much when she asked me what I was sulking about.

She shrugged. 'Your nan seems all right with it.'

This was true, at least.

Mona Lisa

The next day was our only full day in Paris and, naturally, I had a plan that maximised every minute of it.

0800 hours: breakfast

0900 hours: Eiffel Tower

1100 hours: the Louvre

Et cetera et cetera.

I knew Til still thought I was over-controlling things but she didn't bring it up this time. What could I say? It's hard to change a habit of a lifetime overnight.

I gave Nan a rundown of the plan. 'The Loo-vree,' she said slowly, trying carefully to make the sounds. 'Loo-vror. What's that, then?'

'Art gallery thing,' I told her. 'We can see the Mona Lisa?'

'The Mona What-a?'

'You know, it's that really famous painting. Of a woman.' I took out my phone and did a quick image search. 'Here.'

I held it up and Nan squinted at the screen. 'Oh yeah. I know the one. Funny looking, isn't she?'

I shrugged. 'I guess. I don't know who she is.'

'Well, I've seen her now, haven't I? There, in your phone.

Don't need to traipse all the way down to this Loo-vror, do we?'

'Yeah but –'

'Maybe just let your nan do what she wants to do?' Til said, picking lazily at a croissant.

I glared at her. She was meant to be here for support, not rebellion.

'Yes, let me do what I want to do,' Nan echoed.

'What *do* you want to do, Nan?'

'I want to sit outside a nice French cafe and drink as much red wine as they'll bring me and talk to handsome French men.'

So that's what we did. Sort of.

It was a hot day, and since Nan had thrown my plans into disarray I didn't know which direction to walk in. We ambled around the quiet residential streets of the ninth *arrondisement* but Nan kept getting out of breath and asking us to stop every few minutes and eventually Til said, 'All these cafes look the same, Grace. Let's just pick somewhere.

We sat down around a metal table on a pavement corner near the entrance to a tiny park and a metro station. Nan ordered a bottle of red wine ('Why pretend I'm only here for a glass?') and Til and I ordered some random bits of food and drink – chips, *croque monsieurs*, lemonade.

Nan was quiet for a bit, just sipping her wine and staring out across the road at the cars and bikes and smart women with tiny dogs and men carrying ladders and everything else going on.

I was anxious about keeping up my live tweeting of our

mini-break. I'd told my followers I'd be seeing all the sights today, but here I was sitting on the pavement in a perfectly boring street with nothing more to show them than a few tall buildings and some railings.

I took my phone out of my pocket. The image of the Mona Lisa was still in my browser. I saved it to my photos, then I posted it to Instagram:

Nan hanging out with this mysterious lady today #NanOnTour

Who was to know that I hadn't seen it in the flesh? What did it matter anyway? The painting was going to look exactly the same if I went down there and took my own photo, wasn't it?

I checked my phone fifteen minutes later but I had just one like. I was disappointed. Had the people lost interest in #NanOnTour? I decided they were clearly just an uncultured rabble with no appreciation of art. I decided to keep my updates more low-brow from now on. One has to tailor one's material to one's audience, after all.

Til laughed suddenly. I looked at her. 'Paris, eh,' she said, shaking her head. She tilted her head towards the sun and closed her eyes.

I just nodded.

Paris.

Was this it? Was this the moment? The one we were living for? Why did I still feel like I was waiting for something?

I'd felt like this before. I was used to it. I remembered

one specific occasion when I was about nine, Dad had taken Ollie and me to a new leisure centre that had opened up fifteen miles away. The place was heaven – four water slides, a wave machine activated every twenty minutes in the huge oblong pool, a self-service milkshake machine in reception. We'd been there less than fifteen minutes when I turned to Dad wide-eyed and said, 'This is amazing! Can we come here again?' and Dad had laughed and said, 'But we're here now, Gracie. Just enjoy that.' I knew he'd made a good point, but I still struggled with the idea. That this moment was *it*. I wanted some guarantee of a future moment. Now did not seem enough.

As Nan drank her wine, she asked Til about what she planned to do after the summer.

'College,' Til said.

Nan nodded slowly. 'Education, eh. You kids love it, don't you? I couldn't wait to get away. Get a job. Make some money.

'Can't hardly get any jobs without it though,' Til said.

'Not these days, I suppose,' Nan said. 'Do you know, Grace, I said to your cousin Katie the other day, I said, "What exactly is it that you do for a living?" and she sat there with a totally straight face and said, "I'm a Senior Digital Strategy Executive, Nan." I ask you! They make this stuff up, they surely do. Is that what you're going to do, Til, after all this education? Be a Senior Digital Strategy Executive?'

Til laughed. 'Nah. Nothing like that. I'm going to do plumbing. Going to get my NVQ then probably do an apprenticeship. Then, work.'

Nan nodded her approval. 'Sounds very sensible, my girl,' she said. 'You should listen to your mate here, Grace. She'll be looking after herself in no time. None of this living off your mum and dad for the next ten years that you've got planned. Lounging around in grubby student digs smoking funny cigarettes and reading poetry. They indulge you, you know. I wouldn't have been bankrolling that kind of lifestyle for any of mine, I can tell you that for nothing.'

I sat up in my chair. I felt like I'd been ambushed from nowhere. 'I don't want . . . I'm not planning to –'

Nan held her hands up, her palms facing me, and leant back in her chair. 'Nothing to do with me, is it. How you spend your time. How you spend their money. No one's interested in what their old grandma has to say about anything, I know that.'

I was so annoyed by what Nan had said, annoyed on so many levels, that I could hardly get the words out. The idea that I'd been tied to my desk, never having any fun or putting a foot out of line for the last year was because of laziness, because I wanted to live off Mum and Dad for as long as possible, was so far from the truth I didn't even know where to start.

Til stepped in for me. 'My plan ain't no judgement on what other people want to do,' she said. 'I just can't be like my mum, getting paid zero money all her life because she never learnt to do anything that other people need. She gets dropped from a job in a second because there's always a hundred other people who can do the exact same thing queueing up to do it. I just want a van and a toolbox and a little business to call my own.'

Nan nodded and smiled and probably wished that Til was her granddaughter instead of me. I glared at my sandwich.

'Don't sulk,' Til said, as Nan was gesticulating to the waiter that he should bring more wine. 'I thought you did want to sit around in a grubby house reading poetry. That's what uni's all about, isn't it?'

'No!' I said. 'I just wanted a good job in law or business or fashion or something.'

'Fashion?' Til smirked.

'Yeah OK, not fashion.' I paused. 'I don't know. I just wanted to . . . to *be* something.'

'Something better than a plumber?' Til leant on her elbow, one eyebrow raised.

I sighed. 'No. I don't even know. Anyway, I don't want it any more, do I. I told you. I'm done with that. With studying. With waiting. This is life. Now.'

'So.' Til had an amused smile. 'You're not going back to school? No A levels?'

'No,' I said, with more certainty than I felt.

'We'll see,' Til said, leaning back in her chair and tilting her face towards the sun again.

Other Plans

After a while a man came to sit on the table next to us. He was probably about seventy. He had wispy grey hair and was wearing a grey waistcoat over a T-shirt.

He sat down heavily on one of the metal chairs and one of the waiters said something to him in a tone that made me think he went there often and they knew him well. He said something to Nan in French. I didn't understand it so I can't imagine Nan did, but that didn't stop her replying.

'Perfect, isn't it. When you stop rushing around. When you just sit.'

The man said something else. Although it might just have been a noise. It can be hard to tell.

Then he pointed at me and said, 'Daughter?'

Nan laughed. 'Granddaughter. Ain't she lovely?'

I'd never heard Nan say anything like this about me before. She was probably drunk.

'*Ah, oui*,' the man agreed, without really looking at me.

Nan then launched into a monologue. I have no idea how much the man understood but he nodded and smiled and had a twinkle in his eye like he was finding the whole thing rather amusing.

Nan told him how well I did at school, how organised I was and how even as a little kid I was always making lists and plans and keeping everyone in check. At first I felt a bit irritated by all this – the way she was basically making fun of me, right in front of me, to a perfect stranger. But then Nan started talking about how I'd organised this whole trip as a surprise for her and how I'd taken care of everything and made lists and printed out maps and wanted everything to be just right. It was about at this point that I realised Nan wasn't really talking to the man at all. She was looking at him, and he was looking at her, but he probably didn't have a clue what she was saying and she wasn't bothered either way. She was talking to me. For my benefit, anyway.

She was saying thank you.

She was definitely drunk.

Eventually, she stopped pretending to talk to the man at all and he finished his coffee and ambled off.

'I thought you didn't like it here,' I said quietly.

Nan held my hand. 'I like it very much, my love.'

'Oh,' I said. 'That's good then.'

Then Nan leant back in her chair and poured herself another glass of wine from her jug.

'You know, Grace,' she said, looking up at the sky. 'The best things in my life weren't planned. Moving to Scotland in the seventies. Didn't know that was going to happen. Opening the shop. That was never on the cards. Just took a punt. Having your father! That was definitely not planned.'

I wasn't sure you were supposed to say that kind of thing out loud. I wondered if Dad knew.

'You can't plan everything. Else you start to miss out,' Nan went on.

'Life is what happens to us while we're busy making other plans,' Til said suddenly.

'Exactly, my girl,' Nan said, clapping her hands together. 'Who said that?'

'John Lennon,' I said, quick as a flash. I should know – the day of my post-hospital epiphany I'd written out the lyric and sellotaped it to the wall next to my bed.

'Nope,' Nan said. 'Allen Saunders. Don't believe everything you read.'

Happy-Face Nan

Getting a rather drunk Nan up from her rickety chair on the pavement and steering her by the elbow through the uneven streets of Paris to the hotel took some considerable time. She kept stopping to sit down on the metal chairs dotted along the pavements outside bars and restaurant and to make unsolicited comments to the people all around her.

We passed a row of shops and Nan spent a long time gazing at the ornate pastries in the window in wonder, before ordering me in to spend a shocking amount of money on a box of them. Nan ate one, cream spreading from her cheek to her nose as we ambled past some more shops.

'Look at this, girls,' Nan said, stopping abruptly outside one window. 'A butcher's! This is where they get the horses from! Look at it all!' she said, gesturing to the plates of raw meat in a glass case in the window and laughing loudly. 'They got it all here, I can see. Alligators. Hippos. That's a unicorn, I shouldn't wonder!' she said, pointing at something I thought was almost certainly a joint of beef. 'Here, take a photo.' She turned to look at me, her arms outstretched as if presenting the array of meats, a wide smile on her face.

I did as I was told.

'Post that one!' Nan ordered. 'Show everyone what goes on over here!' She laughed again.

It had been a while since I updated the world on #NanOnTour, and I couldn't deny it was quite a funny photo, so I posted it to Instagram with the caption:

My fave happy-face nan

I could feel my phone vibrating with notifications straight away, and by the time we got back to the hotel I had seventy-five likes.

'Weird,' I said to Til, as I sat on the bed and kicked my shoes off. 'Why would so many people like a photo of an old lady outside a shop?'

She took her own phone out and frowned at the screen.

'Ha. Amazing,' she said.

'What?'

'Nice caption.' She tossed her phone over to me.

'Oh no!'

There was the photo of Nan, smiling delightedly at the meat display, her face smeared with the remnants of an expensive French patisserie. And above her, there was my caption, which for some reason my phone had decided to correct from 'My fave happy-face nan' to:

My fave hairy-face man

'Hairy-face man!' I wailed, as Til lay on her back on

her bed, shaking with laughter. 'Why would I call my nan that?'

'I think she'd like it,' Til said. 'She's always talking about her whiskers.'

Til may have been right, but I decided not to risk it by telling her.

On the train home the next day, Nan opened her handbag and tipped out in excess of fifteen croissants, clearly stolen from the continental breakfast buffet at the hotel.

'Seemed a shame to leave them there, in the basket,' she said, ripping one open.

Til put her earphones in and closed her eyes. Nan seemed to be watching her from her seat.

'She's good, that Til,' she said to me. 'You want to stick with her.'

I saw a small smile creep over Til's face. She didn't open her eyes.

PART 4

During which I consider the
unlikely hypothesis that I am,
in fact, a people person

News

Nan died four days after we returned from Paris.

I came home from Til's one evening to find Mum, Dad and Ollie sitting around the kitchen table. They were all staring into space. Ollie was often sitting around staring at nothing, but not Mum and Dad. I knew something was up.

'What?' I said.

'Sit down,' Mum said quietly, so I did.

'What is it?'

'Nan,' Mum said quietly.

'What?' I said again.

Dad rubbed his hand over his face. 'She's gone, Grace.'

'Gone?' I said, although I, of course, knew what he meant.

'It was her heart,' Mum sad. 'Uncle Paul just rang.'

I sat down next to Ollie. It didn't feel real. She'd been fine. The whole time we were away. Fine.

'Was it because we . . . ?' I started. 'We shouldn't have gone to Paris, should we? But she was OK! I thought she was OK.'

Mum shook her head. 'She hadn't been fine for a long time, apparently. She knew she wasn't going to be with us for long.'

'So, the whole time we were there, she knew . . . she knew that . . .'

Dad nodded. 'She knew she wasn't going to be making any more trips.'

'Did she know it was the last time she'd see me?'

Mum looked at Dad. 'I think that's likely,' he said.

I wanted to walk, so I did, with no particular purpose, although I discovered forty minutes later that, in a roundabout way, my feet had carried me to Til's block.

The lift wasn't working – it was never working – so I trudged my way up the nine flights of steps to her flat. Her mum was smoking and watching TV in the lounge as usual.

'Hi,' I called through the open door. She didn't reply.

Til was lying on her bed with her headphones on. She was holding her hand up above her head, turning it over slowly as if she was examining it.

'Do you think I should get a tattoo?' she said when she saw me. 'Like loads of tattoos. Not pointless flowers or Chinese writing. I mean, like, information. Dates I should remember. The periodic table. Not being funny, right, but I've got a lot of skin. Think how much info I could pack in. Like, tide timetables, them charts that show what shapes the stars make . . . I saw this poster once with diagrams of different cocktails. You know, like the ingredients to make them. I could have that. I could –'

'Nan's dead,' I said from the doorway.

Til opened her mouth then closed it again. She shifted herself so she was sitting up on her bed. There was a pause, maybe thirty seconds or more.

'God,' she said. 'Oh, god.'

And then I started to cry.

We didn't cry, Til and I, as a rule. I had never seen Til cry. Not even close. And I think the only time I'd cried – at least with her – was when I'd got my hand trapped in the hinge of the PE cupboard in Year Nine. Til had laughed then. She didn't laugh this time.

I sat down on the end of Til's bed and cried for a solid four and a half minutes. Til edged over to me and put her arm awkwardly around my shoulder.

'Oh, man,' she said. 'Sorry, Gracie. She was so sound.'

I nodded but I couldn't say anything.

Goodbye

Til came with us to the funeral. I didn't ask her to but she wanted to. She looked funny in a way, wearing her black school trousers and a black shirt, which I guessed she must've borrowed from her mum because it was too short in the body. I felt a surge of affection for her when we picked her up outside her block, for making the effort. For wanting to say goodbye to Nan with me.

It was my first funeral. I didn't know what to expect. I'd seen them on films, and seen news footage of grand celebrity funerals. I suppose I assumed it would all be quite dramatic. Ladies in flamboyant black hats with netting covering their faces. Men with red eyes grasping each other tightly. It wasn't really like that at all though.

Everything felt so low-key. Sad, but so ordinary. It didn't seem like we were marking the end of a life. That we were there because Nan – a person who had been very much alive – now simply didn't exist at all.

As we pulled into the crematorium, Mum and Dad chatted quietly about where they should park and if different chapels had designated parking zones or if we could just put the car anywhere. It felt no more momentous than if we'd been pulling up outside Ikea.

It was strange too, seeing everyone outside the crematorium. Lots of them I saw all the time – Uncle Paul, some of my cousins – but others I hadn't seen for years. I'd last seen my cousin Daniel when I was six and he was nine and he'd broken my radio by pouring lemonade into the speaker. He'd been weedy then, no bigger than me. Now he was nineteen, a rugby player, bursting out of his neatly ironed grey shirt. He and Ollie shook hands like proper grown-up men.

There was some awkward chat about what everyone had been up to. I heard several people say it was good to see each other again, just that it was 'a shame about the circumstances'. Dad shook hands with people I didn't recognise and thanked them for coming. Lots of people came over to us and said they were sorry for our loss and we gave sad smiles and said thank you.

Inside the chapel, each of the wooden benches had been laid with 'order of service' cards with Nan's name and photo on the front. Seeing her face there, her eyes looking mischievous, made something turn over in my chest. I thought of her demanding to have her photo taken outside the butcher's in the Paris street. Mum squeezed my hand.

Uncle Paul read the eulogy and Dad said some words too. It was interesting, hearing about everything Nan had done earlier in her life. Everything she and Granddad had done together. Playing in poker tournaments. Fostering wayward teenagers even though they had little kids of their own. I suppose I'd sort of forgotten Nan hadn't been old all her life.

The man leading the funeral – the celebrant, he was called, which seemed an odd term for it – thanked Dad and Paul, and then he said that he had a few words to read from Elizabeth herself. People looked at each other then, twitches of surprise on their faces.

The celebrant began to read.

Hello family, friends, people I used to know, people who have just shown up for the free sandwiches. Welcome to my party. Sorry I couldn't be with you.

I'm seventy-eight now, and the docs reckon I won't make seventy-nine, so I wanted to get a few things down while I've got your attention. Maybe this way some of you will actually listen to me for once.

I've been on this planet for 28,515 days. I just worked it out. It doesn't sound that long really, when you think of how quickly each day goes by. I know I'm lucky to have had as much time as I have. I know a lot of people get far less. But I tell you one thing for sure – it doesn't half go quick! Especially as you get older.

So message number one, family, friends and sandwich-lovers: don't waste any time. You can't afford to.

Decide what you want to do, and then do it. And if you can't decide what you want to do, just do anything. Just do something. And you might find that when you're doing that something, you realise what else you might want to do. Whatever you do, don't waste time sitting around in your underpants waiting for something to come to you. Nothing good ever happened like that.

Mum, Dad and I all looked at Ollie. He just looked down at his lap, rubbing his thumbs together.

What else? Be honest, I think. Tell people you love them while you can. And tell people when they're getting on your wick too, because nothing is a bigger waste of energy than a grudge. Pick your battles wisely, but if you've picked a battle then fight it well. Be brave and kind and fair. Admit when you're wrong.

See the world, if you can. Don't stay in when you could go out. Don't say no when you could say yes.

Remember this: in the end, all that matters is the people you know. Know as many people as you can. Love some of them too, if you can bear to. They're not as bad as you think. They're just trying their best, just like you are.

Goodbye, my loves. Look after each other.

From

Elizabeth

AKA Mum

AKA Aunty Bet

AKA Betty-boo

and

– the celebrant coughed awkwardly and blinked.

AKA your favourite hairy-face man.

Around us people exchanged confused looks and muttered comments about if they'd heard that quite right. I turned around to look at Til, who was sitting in the row behind me, her mouth clamped shut, her eyes shining as she tried to hold in the laughter.

'How did she find out?' I whispered.

Til just shook her head and shrugged, and I too had to try not to laugh in case people thought I was being disrespectful at this sombre occasion, even though I knew Nan wouldn't have been a bit bothered if I had.

In fact, I'm sure she'd have been delighted.

Interpersonal Relationships

That evening, when Mum and Dad dropped Til off, I got out too and went up to her flat with her. She handed me a can of Diet Coke and we sat in silence for a while.

'It's sort of amazing in a way,' Til said slowly. 'Like, the timing I mean.'

I looked at her.

'I just mean,' she said, 'the way you decide to start all this . . . living, all this doing stuff . . . right now. And that meant you decided to see your nan and take her to Paris and do all this once-in-a-lifetime stuff with her.'

I felt myself tearing up. 'I know,' I said. 'It was all too late, wasn't it? Why, why, why did I keep putting her off? I should have gone to see her more. Every Sunday. With flowers and a box of Jaffa Cakes. Why did I leave it till it was too late?'

Til sat up straight and put her hand on my arm. 'No, that's not what I meant at all, man!' she said. 'The opposite. It wasn't too late. It was just in time, wasn't it? You took your nan on her trip of a lifetime, just in time.'

I breathed out heavily and rubbed my eyes. 'I guess.'

'It's totally true, Gracie,' Til said.

We were quiet again while I thought this over. She was right, I decided. Or at least, that was the best way I could look at it now.

'When I started all this – when I decided to start seizing the day, all the days, doing stuff – I thought I'd just do some stupid stuff like the horse riding or whatever. I didn't think it would make me do this. I didn't realise it would be the difference between spending three last, proper, days with my nan and fobbing her off with a postcard and a made-up promise to come and see her at some point.'

Til nodded and we were quiet again for a while. I was thinking.

I sat up suddenly, and turned to look at Til. 'I think this is it, you know. This is what it's all about. The other day, I had this whole conversation with Ollie, about his life and what we were doing and everything. We never talk! That would never have happened if it hadn't been for the new philosophy. And then Paris, my last days with Nan. That wouldn't have happened either. This is what it's about, Til. Don't you think? It's about people. And, like, relationships. Not stupid stuff.'

Til nodded, spinning her can around in her hands. 'Sort of like what your nan said, in her letter.'

Thinking of Nan's letter again, I started to chuckle. 'Hairy-face man. Oh god.'

'I know,' Til said, smiling. 'Proper funny.'

'Maybe I should say something on Twitter,' I said. 'Let them know?'

Til shrugged. 'I guess.'

I opened my phone and found the picture of Nan outside the butcher's. The last photo I'd ever have of her. I posted it to Twitter and Instagram again, this time with the caption:

**Sad to say goodbye to Nan today.
Rest in Peace, Nan. #HairyFaceMan**

I started to laugh again then, because it was such a bizarre thing to be posting, but I was crying too, and the two got all jumbled in together.

The replies rolled in fast:

No! Not Hairy Face Man! #RIP

So sorry, Gracie. Love you.

Aw that's too bad. At least you'll always have Paris.

Til's mum left for work so we went to sit in the lounge and watched some mindless low-budget thriller without really paying attention.

I was thinking – about my conversation with Ollie, and about what Nan had said.

'I think that's what I have to do,' I said randomly as I reached my conclusion.

'What?' Til said.

'I'm going to put some conscious effort into my interpersonal relationships.'

141

Til laughed. 'You sound like that therapist woman who gives advice on the radio. What does that even mean?'

I shrugged. 'I don't know.'

'Do you want to know what I think?' Til said, leaning back on the sofa and resting her feet on the arm.

'No.'

'I think that there's one interpersonal relationship where your conscious efforts should definitely be focused.'

I didn't reply. I knew what she was going to say.

'Sarah,' she said with a grin. 'The lovely Sarah. Lovely library Sarah.'

Library Sarah

Since our conversation in the tent at Camp Matilda, neither Til nor I had mentioned the L word. Any of the L words, I should say. Lesbianism. Love. Ladies. But then that wasn't new. Til had known for ages. I knew she'd known for ages. She knew I'd known she'd known –

You get the picture. We didn't talk about it.

But then the truth was, there wasn't an awful lot to say. I had never known Til to have a boyfriend, although she did go on casual outings with boys, which I suppose could be considered 'dates'.

She'd tell me she'd spent the evening with Milo Wood trying to beat the 2p machines in the arcade while he moaned about how his band were becoming too commercial for his tastes. She'd been to the cinema with Devon Angelo and shared a chilli dog with him on the pier afterwards. I once arrived at her flat just as the Polish boy who cleaned the art room was leaving. I still don't know what exactly had gone on there. We talked about these encounters a little, but not a lot.

'His trousers are too short. Makes him look insane,' Til might say.

Or,

'Did you know he got sacked from work experience for nicking SIM cards and selling them on the internet? Who gets sacked from a job you don't even get paid for?'

That was about the full extent of our analysis, the depth of our heart-to-hearts about our love-lives. Of course, where I was concerned, there really was nothing at all to say. As with most of the other areas of my life, I'd been putting all that business off until after my exams. Romance was not in the plan. Plus, as far as I could tell, I didn't know a single lesbian. Unless you counted Holly Ross's lesbian mums and they weren't exactly my type.

Sarah worked in the library. The library was a place where Til and I spent quite some time, one way or another. It was made up of several different zones, so there was a space for every occasion. If we wanted to work, we could use the computers. If we wanted to listen to music from the dodgy CD borrowing selection, we could sit on the beanbags and use the free headphones. If we wanted to lie on the giant cushions in the sunny patch at the back, we could sit in the kids' section and read books we'd loved when we were seven.

I'd noticed Sarah for the first time around six months ago, when Til and I had been sheltering from the freezing rain one afternoon. She'd been stacking DVDs on the shelf in the Media Centre – a small partitioned area to the right of the library – when the entire plastic display unit had toppled forward, scattering DVDs everywhere.

'Oh, terrific,' Sarah had said, standing in the debris with her hands on her hips. 'Just the look I was going for.'

144

There was something about this – her deadpan delivery, the way her dishevelled blonde hair was piled on her head – that I liked.

As I'd helped her put the display back together she'd alternated between grumbling about how everything she touched disintegrated in her hands and keeping up a sarcastic commentary about the calibre of films that was popular these days.

'I mean, what is this?' She said, holding up the case of *She's the Man*. 'Who thought, I know what I'll do, I'll take *Twelfth Night* and make it all about some moronic teenagers playing some dumbo football match and that will be a movie. Oh yes. What a good idea.'

Sarah chatted to us – to me – every now and then. When she saw me repeatedly watching a video of a kitten falling off a sofa despite the array of history text books spread out in front me of me, she'd said, 'I see it's going well then,' with one eyebrow slightly raised. When an elderly – and apparently quite deaf – woman had trapped her in the corner to tell her loudly about how she'd just this morning got her haemorrhoid cream confused with her denture wash, I'd caught her eye and she'd had to put immense effort into keeping her composure and not collapsing into laughter.

Through our snippets of conversation, I'd found out a few things about Sarah:

She was Welsh. Or at least, she had the accent.

She was seventeen and had just finished her first year of college.

She was studying all the sciences and planned to do medicine afterwards. She frequently despaired of this choice.

Also:

She was gay.

She hadn't told me in so many words – I suppose it would've been a bit of an odd announcement to make in the course of a normal working day as a librarian – but she'd once mentioned an ex in passing and had quite definitely said 'she'.

I don't know if it was finding this out that prompted me to look at her in a new way, or if it was just a growing awareness that I liked her, but the point at which I realised I might have the smallest spark of interest in Sarah was the day I managed to make a total fool of myself.

Great English Classics

I'd often seen her checking out her own books at the end of her shift and she always had some classics in there – *Sense and Sensibility*, *Wuthering Heights*, all that sort of thing. So, quite deliberately, I'd paid a visit to the Classic Literature shelf and selected *Great Expectations* – a book I knew Sarah had just recently borrowed herself.

I'd sat on the beanbags, the cover clearly visible, in the hope that she'd come over and start a conversation. That's exactly what had happened.

'Enjoying it?' she'd said, nodding her head towards the book.

'Oh!' I said, pretending that I'd been so absorbed by the book that I hadn't noticed her coming over. 'Yes, actually. Wonderful.'

'You like the old ones, then? The great English classics?'

I nodded enthusiastically. 'Oh, yes. Anything by Dickens. Or the Brontës. And I love everything that Jane Eyre wrote, of course.'

Sarah frowned slightly. 'Jane Eyre didn't do anything, did she? Well, I mean, she did plenty, falling in love with Mr

Rochester and what have you, but she didn't write anything. She was a character.'

'Oh!' I said again, forcing out a little oh-how-silly-what-a-slip-of-the-tongue laugh. 'Yes, of course. Jane Eyre was a character from . . . from . . .'

'From *Jane Eyre*,' Sarah prompted.

'Yes,' I agreed. 'I meant to say I like the other one. Jane –'

'Jane Austen?'

'Exactly!' I said, laughing again in a feeble attempt to cover my shame. 'Jane Austen. *Pride and Prejudice*, that's my favourite.'

My relief at having been able to pluck the name of one of Jane Austen's works so quickly from the air turned to panic when I realised that I'd just left myself open to an in-depth discussion on a book I'd never read. I hadn't even seen the film all the way through.

Luckily, I was off the hook. Sarah scrunched up her nose. 'Bit long for me, those ones. Too many words. I'm just like, get to the point why don't you!'

I was surprised. 'But you're always getting them out?'

I immediately regretted letting Sarah know I'd been monitoring her selections like this, but she didn't seem to notice.

'Yeah, they're for my mum,' she said. 'She loves all those. She's got more patience than me. And she hasn't got four A levels to study for!'

I laughed. 'Yeah. Course.'

Still, my attempt to impress Sarah can't have completely failed because since that day, she'd spoken to me more often, and for longer each time.

She'd sit down beside me on the cushions sometimes and chat to me while she ate an apple, or she'd flop down heavily, sigh and say things like, 'I tell you what, sometimes this is the best job in the world but sometimes it's the absolute worst,' before launching into a story, told in hushed conspiratorial tones, about how Tony, the library manager, kept muddling people's reservations so Sarah often found herself presenting seven-year-old boys with knitting pattern collections or smart elderly gentlemen with books called, *Some Like it Hot: A Guide to Spicing Up Your Sex Life*.

By April, I was pretty sure I was into her. Not in the slightly mad obsessive way that I had been with sixth-form Amelia who helped Reggie with his maths or Elodie the mysterious French-exchange girl, but I liked her. I wanted her to be my friend, I suppose. Maybe more than a friend, but I felt OK about it. I didn't feel like a crazy stalker like I had when I'd waited at a bus stop for over an hour, letting bus after bus pass me by in the hope that if I hovered around long enough, Elodie might need to go somewhere, and so would come and ask me for help reading the timetable.

What I hadn't really ever given any thought to though, was the idea that Sarah might be at all interested in me.

Requited

'She is so into you, man,' Til said, throwing grapes up into the air and trying to catch them in her mouth.

'What?' I said, squinting at her. 'She is n— what? Why would you say that?'

'Number one: she's always talking to you. And if I come over when she is, she looks annoyed and gets up. Number two: she's always giving you lesbian books to read. Number three: she looks at you, right in the eyes. That's the real giveaway.'

'Where else is she supposed to look? My knees?'

'But it's like this.' Til scooted over to my end of the sofa, sat directly in front of me, pushed her face so it was a few centimetres away from mine and stared at my eyes without blinking. 'See? That's totally flirting.'

I laughed. 'That is not flirting.'

'Basically is though.'

I thought about this for a moment. I had admired plenty of girls from afar but this was the first time I had ever had reason to believe that a genuine lesbian may be interested in doing any genuine lesbianing with me.

It was very interesting news.

Although I wasn't yet totally convinced.

'But how would she know to? Flirt with me, I mean? I'm like . . . incognito. She could be barking up the wrong tree, for all she knows.'

Til shrugged. 'Dunno. She must have one of those gaydars. Do you all get one? Do you have one?'

I looked down at myself. 'I don't know. I don't think so. Maybe I need to get one.'

'Not sure you can just pick one up from Argos, Gracie. You obviously need to put some practice in. So far, my gaydar is outstripping yours by a mile.'

I looked out of the window for a minute, thinking about all this. I realised my natural impulse was, as ever, to tell Til she was talking rubbish, keep hanging around the library hoping Sarah might engage me in the odd chat, but essentially, to do nothing.

But then, doing nothing wasn't part of the new plan, was it? No longer was I an avoider, a procrastinator, a coward. I was a plunge-taker and a go-getter. I couldn't start chickening out now, just because it was getting scary. I'd swung from a giant metal arch with my trousers round my ankles, for goodness' sake!

Surely this wasn't beyond me?

Not Indifferent

I got to the library early the next day.

So early, in fact, that I had to hover around pretending to look at my phone until someone came to unlock the automatic doors. This was partly because I knew that Sarah was working the morning shift, but mostly because I knew that the longer I dwelled on if and when and how to speak to her, the more likely it was that I'd just bottle it altogether.

I didn't really have a plan. I wasn't totally sure what I was hoping to achieve. I think I was going to ask Sarah out on a date. But then, was that something people actually did? Did people really go on 'dates' still? This wasn't a world I'd been involved with before.

I hoped that I could just turn up at the library and some easy, friendly chat with Sarah would naturally develop. And this time I'd be finely attuned to any flirtatious undertones and be ready to pounce (figuratively speaking). In short, I suppose my grand scheme to ask Sarah out was basically to hope that she asked me out, and that all I'd have to do is accept graciously.

As a plan, it was perhaps a little on the optimistic side.

But the point was, I had to ramp things up a notch, so that we could progress from our current librarian/customer dynamic to people who were choosing to spend leisure time together. Even without any romantic intentions though, it seemed quite a leap.

I wasn't even sure it was allowed. Were there some rules about ethics in this situation? Like a doctor and patient? Was there some invisible line that could never be breached between a librarian and a book-browser? I decided not.

The first difficulty I encountered was looking nonchalant. Nonchalant isn't a look I've ever really been able to pull off. I can do stressed or keen or awkward but I've never been able to create the impression that I'm feeling cool or relaxed or indifferent, not even when I am feeling cool or relaxed or indifferent. And when I walked into the library and immediately found myself looking at Sarah as she pushed the returns trolley between the shelves, I realised just how non-indifferent I felt about it all. I felt quite different indeed.

Oh my dear lord she was attractive.

I don't know if I'd known it all along or if it was just because Til had put the idea in my head that Sarah might like me, but I suddenly realised that I really wanted to kiss her. It was quite a surprising sensation to have first thing in the morning in the glass walkway outside the library gift shop. I was just looking at her, looking at her cute confused expression she made as she couldn't work out why the wheels of her trolley were stuck. Her hair was all messy on top of her head. She had very nice teeth.

The thunderbolt realisation that I did actually quite like her, and that I wasn't only going along with this whole asking-her-out episode to prove to Til – and myself – that I was serious about grabbing life by the horns, made the whole operation even more complicated.

Such a Fan

Sarah had moved over to the Media Centre, and was untangling the headphones cords before putting them back in their holders. I approached the CD unit and pretended to be engrossed in reading the backs of the CDs. I had my back to her, so she made me jump when she appeared next to me.

'Oh god, I love those guys,' she said.

I looked up and saw her nod towards the CD in my hand. I turned it over. The Sneaks.

'I saw them at Reading,' she went on, 'at like eleven o'clock in the morning or something, when no one knew who they were. And I said to my mate Davey, "They're amazing, they are," and then what do you know? Two weeks later they're on Radio 1 and then they're everywhere. That one's OK but their best album is *The Office Stereo.*'

'Oh yeah, I love that one,' I heard myself saying.

But why was I saying that? I had never heard of The Sneaks. I had never heard any of their albums. I suppose it just seemed like a good thing to say to keep the conversation going.

Sarah's eyes lit up. 'Isn't it lush?' she said. 'Like when the intro kicks in on "Endless Ends" I'm just like . . .' She opened her eyes wide and shook her head rapidly from side to side, like someone with their head in a washing machine.

'Yeah,' I agreed, smiling. 'Totally.'

Oh god. What was I talking about?

'You know they're playing at Concorde 2, the day after tomorrow. But the tickets all sold like *that*.' She clicked her fingers. 'So gutting.'

'Oh, I know someone who can get tickets,' I said.

WHY? Stop talking, Grace. You have actually gone mad.

Sarah's mouth fell open and she looked at me, blinking. 'Shut. Up,' she said. 'You serious?'

I nodded. What else could I do?

My claim wasn't complete, one-hundred-per-cent fiction – although it was close – because I was thinking of Niall Gregson, who I sat next to in maths and who worked in Reboot Records where tickets were sold. But I had no idea if there was any truth whatsoever in the idea that he could get me tickets to a sold-out gig. It was, I immediately realised, highly unlikely. But the conversation had taken on a life of its own. I couldn't back-track now.

'We should go, shouldn't we?' Sarah said, her eyes still shining. 'We can't *not* go. I can pay. If you can get the tickets, I'll pay. How amazing would that be?'

It was at this point that I realised that my dubious plan was actually working: Sarah was asking *me* out. The one small problem was that I'd managed to orchestrate the situation

156

only by saying something that I was pretty certain was a monumental lie.

But what to do? Back out and throw the opportunity away, or plough on and hope for the best? I decided on the latter.

'It would be amazing,' I agreed. And I meant it. Despite never having heard of the The Freaks or The Sneaks or whatever they were called, I had the definite feeling that seeing them with Sarah would be pretty special. 'Leave it with me, I'll see what I can do.'

Leave it with me? I don't think I'd ever said something so commanding, so self-assured. I have no idea if I managed to pull the sentence off. If I did, then I'm a better actor than I thought I was.

'Ah, brilliant!' Sarah said. 'Tell you what, I'll give you my number and you can let me know if you can sort it?'

Sarah was giving me her number. Just volunteering it. I hadn't even asked.

She reeled off the digits, I typed them into my phone, then she said she'd better get on and wheeled her trolley back over to the main desk.

I was left there, The Sneaks album still in my hand, wondering how on earth I was going to get myself out of this.

Reboot

I saw Niall as soon as I went into Reboot Records. He was leaning on the counter, tapping his pen in time to the music and looking bored.

'Oh all right, Grace?' he said when he saw me. 'How's it going?'

'Yeah, OK,' I said, looking up at the whiteboard above his head. This was the board where they kept a list of all the local gigs together with venues and ticket prices. I found The Sneaks easily enough – Concorde 2, the day after tomorrow, just as Sarah had said – but there was a big red 'Sold Out' sticker over the price.

'What you looking for?' Niall said, following my eye line up the board.

'The Sneaks,' I said.

Niall laughed. 'You're about four months too late in that case. That one sold out about six minutes after they went on sale.'

I sighed. It wasn't exactly surprising news. 'How can they be *that* good?'

Niall shrugged and started fiddling with a roll of till

receipt paper. 'Dunno. They're only OK. They just don't do many gigs.'

'Can you get me tickets?' I blurted out suddenly. I immediately wished I'd eased into the request more gently, buttered Niall up with some small talk about how his exams went, or how nice his hair looked or something.

Niall laughed. 'Me? You're joking, aren't you? I just do the till.'

I frowned and chewed on my lip for a minute. Then I turned and looked at him. 'Niall,' I said seriously. 'I really, really need to get tickets to that show. It's not for me. Well, not *just* for me. It's for someone else. It's life and death, basically.'

I don't know why I added that. I could think of no plausible way I could justify such a dramatic classification. Luckily Niall didn't question it. I suppose he was used to dealing with obsessive music fans. He wasn't to know this was nothing to do with music.

Niall shrugged. 'Online, I guess. You won't find them on eBay or anything because they shut all that down, but people might be selling them informally. Facebook, Twitter, whatever.'

'Right, OK,' I said, looking up at the list again. It all sounded a bit ambitious. I had a horrible feeling I was going to have to text Sarah and tell her that I hadn't been able to get tickets after all. And then I might as well tell her I'd never heard of the stupid band. And in fact, had never been to an actual music gig before, unless you count the time I went with Dad and Nan to see a Pavarotti tribute act in St

159

Barnabus church and Nan had sung through the first half and snored through the second half before declaring him 'totally tone deaf' and walking out just before the end.

Niall took my number and said he'd call me if they had any returns but warned me, 'It's never going to happen,' which was at least honest.

Better than Nothing

When I got home I searched every conceivable corner of the internet for anyone trying to offload spare tickets for Thursday night. I didn't want to publicly post that I was looking for tickets in case Sarah saw and realised how desperately I was having to scrabble around to try to fulfil my promise.

There were people talking about the gig all right – people looking forward to it and people who had been to other gigs and blah blah blah – but no one who could actually get me any tickets.

I needed to think of a back-up plan. I was just running through the options and wondering if I could take Sarah to an alternative venue to see a different band and somehow persuade her the whole thing had been an enormous administrative error when my mobile rang.

It was a local number. My first thought was that it was Sarah, calling from the library, although there was no reason why that would be the case.

'Hello?'

'Hi, Grace. It's Niall. How much do you love me?'

I paused. What? Had something I'd said during our three-minute interaction about tickets led Niall to believe I was interested in him? Maybe it was because I'd come straight from the library, from Sarah. Maybe I hadn't shaken off the aura of flirtation and it had somehow spilled into my conversation with Niall. Oh god.

'Pardon?'

'I've got a ticket here. Some guy just came to pick his up and it turned out he'd ordered one too many so I refunded him one. I can't keep it for long because I'm not meant to reserve them but it's yours if you can pay now.'

'I can pay now,' I said without thinking. Just one wasn't ideal but it was fifty per cent of the way there. One was better than none. Probably.

Twenty minutes later I was back in Reboot Records.

'You know what you could do if you can't find another one before Thursday,' Niall said as I paid him for the solitary ticket. 'Just hang around out the front for a bit. There's often people trying to offload one last minute.'

'Really?' I said. This was interesting news. It was a risky strategy but I didn't have any other options.

When I got home I texted Sarah.

Got the tickets ☺

She replied a few minutes later.

Oh my GOD!!
I'll call you when I finish my shift to arrange!!

162

Date Night

By the time Sarah rang later that afternoon, I'd already decided not to mention the fact that I had technically only managed to source one ticket. If I did, I thought it was likely that Sarah would say that, of course, I must go, and she would miss out this time. Even if I could persuade her to take it, I still wouldn't be able to go with her, and two people doing the same thing at the same time is surely the most basic of principles for a date.

I arranged to meet Sarah at Concorde 2 on Thursday evening and that was that. I had arranged a date. An actual date with someone I was actually into, like the spontaneous, life-grabbing, enthusiastic burgeoning lesbian that I apparently now was.

As 8 p.m. on Thursday approached, I got steadily more apprehensive about how I was going to deal with the fact that there were two of us going to an event with only one ticket between us. I kept telling myself that I would deal with the situation as I got to it – which was, after all, in keeping with my new mindset – but as things stood, I had no idea how that dealing might manifest itself.

I – spontaneously, of course – bought a cool T-shirt from a vintage place in The Lanes. It was sort of kitsch ironic My Little Pony thing. I thought it would make me look cool, but not pretentiously so. Cool, but with the added bonus of a sense of humour.

When I got out of the shower, I opened my drawer to find some clean pants, only to find it completely empty. I was used to my supply being low due to Paddy's fastidious fancy-dress habits, but he'd never cleaned me out completely before.

'Paddy!' I called, marching across the landing to his bedroom. I pushed the door open. 'Paddy, have you got my knick— PADDY!'

Paddy was sitting in the middle of the bedroom floor in front of the small inflatable paddling pool decorated with shells that Dad had bought him. The pool was filled with water and what smelt like washing-up liquid, together with a soaking wet mass of fabric.

'Cleaning them for you, Gracie,' Paddy explained earnestly. He was stirring his laundry with the giant wooden pencil we'd bought him from the Sea Life Centre.

'Paddy! That's all my underwear! What am I supposed to wear now?'

He reached in and took out one soaking pair and held it out to me, soapy water dripping onto his carpet. 'Here go?' he said, smiling innocently.

I ignored his offering and marched into Mum and Dad's room, struggling to hold my towel up. But alas, Mum's pants had met a similar fate. There was not a wearable pair of female pants in the entire house and I was forced to seriously contemplate the (surely rather presumptuous) option of going commando on a first date.

I couldn't though; I just couldn't do that. It was unhygienic apart from anything. I had one last option. It wasn't ideal, but desperate times, desperate measures.

'Ollie!' I knocked on his bedroom door and then walked straight in. Ollie was in bed, playing his PlayStation. 'Ollie, do you have any pants that are both clean and not too awful?'

He frowned. 'What?'

'I need to wear your pants. It's an emergency. Believe me, I would not be asking otherwise.'

'What? No. Don't be a freak.'

'Seriously, Ol. I need to go out and Paddy has ruined all mine.' I went over to Ollie's top drawer and rummaged around. I found a pair that didn't seem too oversized and flappy, covered in little illustrations of Buzz Lightyear.

'These.' I held them out. 'Are they clean?'

Ollie shrugged. 'Probably.'

I returned to my bedroom and put them on, trying not to think about the weirdness of sharing underwear with my big brother. Actually, they were rather comfortable.

Overcome with misplaced confidence, I decided to have a go with Mum's liquid eyeliner. Why I thought a first date – if that was indeed what this was – was a suitable occasion for this kind of cosmetic boldness I don't know and, somewhat predictably, even with the careful guidance of a YouTube tutorial entitled 'Smokin' Eyes', I struggled.

It was getting both eyes to match that proved the biggest challenge. I could get my eyes to look acceptable on their own, but as a pair they were wonky. And the thing about eyes is that they do tend to present as a pair, ideally speaking. Unless I wanted to spend the evening turning my head rapidly from side to side like a defective robot, showing Sarah only one eye at a time, I was going to have to even them out. And the only way I could see to do this was to keep adding a little more on either side until the thick black lines were roughly equal. By the time I was satisfied my eyes were just about matching, I resembled a sleep-deprived panda.

I grabbed my new ironic, cool-but-with-a-sense-of-humour T-shirt from the carrier bag on my bed. It was only as I was pulling it on that I noticed the label at the collar. 'Little Snugglers, age 7–8'. My cool ironic T-shirt was, in fact, a child's pyjama top. I wavered for a moment, before deciding to pull it on regardless. Maybe Sarah wouldn't notice. And anyway, I wasn't exactly spoilt for options.

I added my jeans to the ensemble and stood back in front of my mirror to take in the full effect.

I was a sleep-deprived panda with jaundiced limbs in a child's pyjama top and Buzz Lightyear pants.

I hoped Sarah would be able to look beyond first impressions.

Sold Out

Sarah was already there when I came down the cliff-side steps that led to the entrance to Concorde 2, which is exactly what I'd hoped for when I'd made myself walk three times around my block to make sure I was fashionably, nonchalantly late.

She was leaning against the railings between the prom and the beach, typing on her phone. She must've sensed me approaching because she looked up.

She smiled and pushed herself off the railings towards me.

'I'm so excited,' she said, grinning. 'In fact, I'm so excited I'm almost nervous. Is that mad?'

Her Welsh accent was particularly noticeable on the word nervous. Ner-vus. I found myself repeating it out loud. 'Ner-vus.'

She smiled again. 'You too, huh?' Then she laughed. 'Or are you just laughing at my accent?'

Oh god. I hadn't meant to. What kind of way was that to start the evening?

'No, I –'

Sarah just laughed. And as it happened, I was nervous. Sickeningly so. Although it had precisely nothing to do with how great The Sneaks allegedly were and everything to do with the fact that I was there and she was there and we were one ticket down and I still had no idea how I was going to get the evening to work out without looking like a complete idiot.

I took the sole ticket in my possession out of my pocket and handed it to Sarah.

'Here you go then. Guard it with your life, et cetera et cetera.'

She took it from me, gazed down at it for a moment, then said, 'Come here, you absolute legend,' and, rather to my surprise, pulled me into a hug.

I still wasn't really sure what the dynamic was between us. Officially, we'd been library staff and library patron. We were now apparently socialising so I suppose that took us up one level – to what? Friends? Acquaintances who liked (pretended to like) the same music? But then there was this business with Til claiming Sarah liked me, and I definitely liked her, so was this a date? How would I ever find out?

If Til had been there I would have put these queries to her, and she would have undoubtedly responded with something along the lines of, 'Shut up talking about it and just get on with doing it,' so that's what I decided to do.

'Shall we go in and get a drink or something then?' Sarah said. 'Support starts in fifteen minutes.'

'Sure,' I said, because there was nothing else to say. I looked over in slight panic to where the short woman in a black leather jacket was standing at the door ripping the corners off people's tickets as she let them in.

We made our way over.

'Oh, wait a sec,' I said suddenly.

Sarah turned to look at me.

'I've just seen someone I want to say hi to.' I waved my arm vaguely in the direction of a few groups of people who were hanging around outside, smoking or perhaps waiting for friends to join them. 'You go in. I'll catch you up.'

Sarah frowned slightly. 'Oh, it's OK. I'll wait.'

'No, no!' I said, actually putting my hand on her back as if to guide her. 'I just want to . . . just got something to talk about . . .'

'Oh!' Sarah said, her eyes widening. 'Oh, I get it. Private chat. Um, OK, cool. I'll get us a drink.'

As I watched Sarah make her way in through the door, the short woman tearing her ticket, I cringed and put my hands over my face. This was a brilliant start. Within three minutes of meeting her, I'd basically told Sarah to get lost so I could talk to someone else. Still, I didn't have time to dwell on how I could've handled the situation better. I had a mission.

I approached the nearest group of people to me. They were three boys, probably a bit older than Ollie, who looked like they'd come in fancy dress as each other. They all had tight T-shirts decorated with thick primary-coloured stripes, black skinny jeans and hair that flopped over their foreheads.

'Um, hi,' I said, and they stopped talking to look at me. 'I don't suppose you've got a spare ticket at all?'

They all mumbled a range of 'no, sorry' type comments before turning back to their conversation. I didn't have time to hang around. I moved onto the next group. They were older this time, two couples, I guessed by the hand-holding arrangements.

I repeated my query but, once again, got nowhere.

I started to panic. This was a sold-out gig. If people had a spare ticket they surely would've sold it for a hundred pounds on the internet already. Sarah was in there and soon she'd wonder where I was. She'd think I'd just abandoned her, for my mysterious friend outside who I wanted to have a private chat with.

Onwards I went. My next target was another group of boys. They were rowdier than the first. Drunk, I suspected.

''Ello,' one boy said I'd before I had a chance to say anything. 'My niece has got those pyjamas.' He nodded towards my top.

I was deciding whether to protest that they weren't pyjamas, or to just ride it out, and agree that yes, I was indeed edgy enough to wear child's pyjamas to a gig, when out of the corner of my eye, I saw Sarah step around the side of the building. She had a drink in each hand and she was looking up and down the wall, squinting as she looked into the sun.

She was looking for me.

Oh god.

Busted

She saw me and smiled a slightly unsure smile.

'You ready?' she called, making her way tentatively over to me, obviously not sure if I was still in the midst of the private conversation that I hadn't wanted her present for.

'Um . . .' I said.

The hairy boy spoke next. ''Ello,' he said. 'I was just complimenting your mate's pyjamas.'

'Huh?' Sarah said, and I pulled my jacket over my chest.

We all stood around awkwardly for a minute. I suppose the boys were wondering if I was going to make my reasons for approaching them known. I suppose Sarah was wondering if I was going to either introduce her to them, or end the conversation and follow her inside. I was wondering what on earth I could do next.

'I'm Sarah,' Sarah said eventually and held out her hand.

The hairy man shook it. 'I'm Jack,' he said.

'How do you know Grace?' Sarah asked, all smiles, but no doubt wondering why I was so socially inept that she was having to take control of proceedings.

Jack blinked. 'I don't.'

'Oh, OK.' Sarah looked at me.

More awkward silence.

Oh god.

I realised there was literally nothing I could do. There was no way out of this. I had to come clean.

'I don't have a ticket,' I said quietly.

Sarah looked at me, her head on one side. 'Huh?'

I took a few steps away from hairy Jack and his friends so as not to have to tell the whole pathetic story with an audience. They seemed to have lost interest in us by this point anyway.

'I don't actually have a ticket,' I said again. 'That's why I can't go in. I only had one.'

Sarah looked at me, confused. 'But . . . how do you . . . ?' She looked down at her pink wristband – the one they'd given at the door in exchange for her ticket. 'Oh god!' she said, starting to tug at it. 'You gave me your one ticket! I can't take that. Here. You take it.'

I held up my hands and stepped away from her. 'No! No, that's not what I meant. I just tried to get two tickets but I couldn't so I got one and then I thought I'd get another one down here, from someone outside or something but –'

'But why did you say you'd got the tickets if you . . . if you hadn't?'

I just shook my head and fiddled with my sleeve. 'I don't know. I got myself in a situation.'

Sarah was laughing. 'You're so weird.'

'I know.'

'But that is *so* something I would do.'

'Really?'

'Totally. I always say things without thinking and just hope I can work out the details later. All the time! Look, let's go and sit down there.' She pointed to the beach where a few people were sitting on the stones, some with cans in their hands, some poking disposable barbecues. 'We've got drinks. We can probably hear the band from there anyway. Sort of.'

I looked down at the beach doubtfully. 'I don't know,' I said. 'You've got a ticket. You should go and use it.'

Sarah shook her head firmly. 'Nope. I'd rather be with you.'

I stopped then, and she stopped, and we just looked at each other. 'Really?' I said. And that was a moment. There was a shift then.

'Really,' she said quietly.

Then we got over the moment and Sarah strode off down to the stones and I followed her.

To Infinity

I assumed that if there was to be any time for talking that evening it would largely be focused around the band. With this in mind, I'd done some not-insubstantial research so as not to give myself away.

I could tell you that The Sneaks formed in 2014 after the lead singer, Jake English, met the bassist, Kyle Noro, when they were both working at the Bridgehouse Cinema in Nuneaton. I could tell you that their first single was 'We Will Watch' but that it only charted at number forty-five and it wasn't until their follow-up, 'Another Morning', that people started to get interested. I could tell you all sorts of other facts and figures but as it turned out, I didn't need any of them. On balance, I was quite glad about this because I'm not sure reeling off Wikipedia pages has ever been the most effective seduction technique.

We talked generally about what we'd be doing this summer and Sarah was impressed by how much I'd managed to fit in already.

'You're kind of a do-er,' she commented.

'Now I am,' I said. 'I'm trying, anyway. It's new.'

And then I told her all about my near-death experience, my epiphany and my new philosophy to live every day as if it were my last.

Sarah laughed. 'I get that. I get that feeling. When my exams finished last month I didn't even want to plan what I was having for lunch. I just lay on the sofa watching CBeebies for, like, two solid days. Sometimes you just want to relax.'

'It's more than that though,' I said. 'This isn't just relaxing after exams. I've just realised how badly I was doing at life! Like, letting it pass me by. I was pinning everything on the future like this bit was some kind of warm-up. But *this* is my life! Now! What if I get run over tomorrow?'

'What if you don't?'

'Well . . . then I'll continue having a very nice time, thank you very much.'

Sarah just laughed and lay back on the stones. I joined her and our heads were close together.

'Have you had a girlfriend before?' she asked.

I was slightly taken aback by the forthrightness of the question.

'No one special,' I said vaguely. Sarah turned her head to look at me and I did the same, so we were lying on the stones with our faces a few inches apart. She raised one eyebrow slightly.

'OK, fine,' I relented. 'No one at all.'

Sarah laughed. She didn't ask anything else, so I turned my head back and carried on looking up at the sky.

We could hear the music pretty clearly from where we were. There was a lot of drumming and the words sounded something like 'That's not my flamingo, you're not a flamingo', which seemed an improbable lyrical selection, but I couldn't ask Sarah about it as I was supposed to be a huge fan of The Sneaks and therefore completely *au fait* with all their songs, flamingo-based or otherwise.

Sarah turned over so she was lying on her front, leaning on her elbows, and I turned and looked at her.

And then she kissed me. On the lips.

I was so surprised I didn't know what to do. I just stayed completely still, like someone having a splinter removed from their face.

'Oh,' I said when she moved away. 'Thanks.'

Sarah burst out laughing. 'Thanks!'

She was quiet for a moment. Then she began, 'Grace . . .'

'Yeah?' I looked at her, straight into her eyes. I wasn't sure what was going to happen next. I really quite wanted her to kiss me again, so I stayed in position to make it easier for her. Then I thought she might be about to tell me she loved me. It was a bit early for all that but I have heard that lesbians can be intense. Would I have to say it back though? I wasn't sure that I –

'Are you wearing Buzz Lightyear boxer shorts?'

I spun round and saw the thick elastic waistband of Ollie's boxers clearly protruding above the top of my jeans.

'Oh god,' I groaned.

'To infinity and beyond!' Sarah read from the slogan circling my waist.

'Oh god,' I said again.

Sarah laughed and as there didn't seem to be anything

else I could do, I explained Paddy's preference for wearing girls' pants with his princess dresses and how this had led to my predicament. She laughed again and I tried, without much success, to hide the ridiculous pants from view.

Eventually it got cold on the beach and the crowd started to spill out of Concorde 2 and we decided we too should make our ways home.

'Sorry about tonight,' I said, as we reached the corner where we had to go our separate ways. 'I don't know how I managed to mess it up so royally.'

'Oh, enough of that,' Sarah said. 'It was great.'

Then she leant forward, kissed me on the cheek and said, 'I'll see you soon, OK?'

'Sure, OK,' I said, and managed to resist the temptation to shout 'WHEN?' after her, as she gave me a sort of half-wink and strode off down the road, her bag swinging over her shoulder.

I lay in bed that night typing out texts and deleting them.

Sorry again –

No. I'd already apologised. Let it go now.

Thanks for the great night –

No. Bland. I needed to think of something sparkier.

When shall we meet again? –

No, no, no. Too desperate. A bit stalkery.

When I still had my phone in my hand, Sarah's name flashed up. A new message. I almost deleted it in my hurry to open it.
Her text was just three words:

I like you

An Outing

The next morning, I woke up unnaturally early feeling unnaturally amazing. I could hear birds singing and there was a child laughing somewhere in the distance and the world seemed full of unadulterated joy.

I called Til.

'Yeah?'

'Til, the world is full of unadulterated joy!'

'You pulled the library bird?'

'Yep! She likes me. She messaged me. She said "I like you".'

'Smooth.'

'I've decided. I'm going to tell Mum and Dad today. I might want to bring Sarah round, so I need to prep them.'

'Out and proud, eh?'

'So out.'

'I'm going back to sleep.'

She hung up and I laughed at how grumpy she was.

Mum and Dad were sitting up in bed reading the newspaper. I went into their bedroom and sat at the end of their bed in between them, my legs crossed.

'Hello, love,' Mum said, looking up from her crossword only briefly.

'I have something to tell you,' I said. Importantly, because it was important.

They both looked up. Mum folded her paper and rested it on her lap. She looked serene. 'Yes?'

'I'm a gay. I mean, gay. A lesbian. A gay lesbian.'

They both kept looking at me. Dad was smiling. Mum took a sip of her tea and smiled.

They didn't say anything. They just sat there.

Why weren't they speaking? Were they in shock?

And I was shocked myself actually, about that. Mum and Dad have always been very chilled on the gays front. Mum's friend Alison at work has a gay son and Mum's always telling me about his plans for his enormous gay wedding. Dad's cousin Monica is a lesbian and although Dad doesn't like her I thought that was because she smokes in the house without asking and because she always pulls Dad's head downwards and laughs at his bald patch. I never got the feeling that it was because she was living in a flat in Croydon with a cello player called Karen.

'I know it's a lot to take in,' I said.

Maybe they were worried about the grandchildren situation. Or maybe they were just enormous closet homophobes and I'd never realised. This was a startling development. I immediately imagined myself on a well-publicised crusade. I could write a blog and post videos to YouTube all about how my previously loving and supportive parents had turned out to be secret bigots and how I was working hard to turn that around through education and patience.

They were still looking at me.

'Yes, love, go on?' Mum said.

'What do you mean "go on"?'

'Tell us the end of the story. You're a lesbian and you've met a girl you're planning to marry? You're a lesbian so you're going to put yourself forward as LGBT ambassador for your school?'

'What do you mean, the story? There is no story! It's just a revelation. A confession I had to get off my chest. Well, not a confession because that sounds like it's bad and it's nothing to be ashamed of, Mum and Dad! It's just a bombshell, that's all. A shock.'

Mum and Dad looked at each other, frowning slightly. Then Mum put her tea down next to the bed. 'But it's not a bombshell, Gracie. We've known for ages. Are you drunk?'

'What? No! What do you mean, known for ages? How is that true or even possible?'

Dad looked at Mum and then back at me. 'Well, when you were a little girl you used to cut out all those photos of the girls from my magazines and put them all over your wall. We thought you liked the clothes at first, but you didn't seem remotely interested in clothes yourself.'

'What? That means nothing.'

'Then there was that foreign student girl we used to get in to babysit when you were eight or nine. What was her name? Audrey? French girl. You would not leave her alone!'

'I just thought she was nice!' I protested. Although, I must

181

say, I was interested to note that I had apparently always had a thing for the French.

'I remember Dad saying to me then – she's going to have an eye for the ladies, that one.'

Dad chuckled fondly at the memory.

'Ugh! Dad! Please!'

'And then what was all that about Angelina Jolie? Last summer when they had that Brad and Angelina season on Channel 4, you were forever saying how beautiful she was.'

'Once! I said it once!'

'I'm sure it was at least three times, love,' Mum said serenely. 'And so we thought that was it – that was you telling us. We didn't want to make a song and dance about it! We were trying to be sensitive. No one wants to have to hammer home a point, do they. I didn't want to make you spell it out. That's why I've been dropping a word in people's ears for you, to save you the faff of having to get round everyone.'

'What? What people?'

'Oh, well, just family really, anyone who might have an interest in what you're up to. Ollie already knew, obviously. Auntie Kath and Uncle Paul because you're not always around when they come over so I took the opportunity when they were down for Easter lunch. They were telling us about how their Benji was playing table tennis for Bedfordshire now so I just dropped in that you were a lesbian. You know, just exchanging news. Then there was your nan . . .'

'God rest her soul,' Dad added.

'God rest her soul,' Mum repeated. 'Then, you know, the

other cousins. I expect Kath told Uncle Jim and Auntie Louise because you know she doesn't have anything interesting in her life, so this would've given her something to talk about. Remember when they nearly won those tickets for that cruise and they told us eight separate times about how close they'd come? Imagine if they'd actually won!'

'Anyone else?' I said, getting off the bed and standing at the foot of it with my hands on my hips. 'Anyone else you've told my business before I'd even worked out it was my business at all?'

Mum frowned, thinking. 'Oh,' she said after a moment. 'Hilary from Pilates. She kept going on and on about how her Flora is so independent and determined and how she's going to live in Cambodia for three months to dig a well or build an orphanage or something and one day I'd had enough so I just said, "Well, my Grace is a lesbian, you know." That shut her up. Couldn't compete with that.'

I ignored the complete lack of sense being made here.

'Right. Great. This is all brilliant.'

'Why are you mentioning it now, anyway, love?' Dad said. 'Is there someone you want to bring home? I can make chilli if you like. And nachos! Proper nachos. I'll get some real avocados when I go to Tesco.'

'No!' I said. 'There isn't anyone.' I'd gone off the idea of telling them about Sarah. 'You don't need to buy avocados.'

'What is the plural of avocado?' Mum said. 'Is it avocados? Or is it just avocado? Like sheep?'

I left them discussing this thorny issue and trudged across the landing and back into bed. I was annoyed at them, I thought, for ruining my big moment. But then I realised I was really annoyed at myself. I was the last one to cotton on to everything!

I was doing life so slowly that other people were having to drag me through these key milestones while I lagged behind, being the last to work out what was going on. If I carried on like this, what else would happen? Would I be telling people I was pregnant as the midwife had her head up my skirt, pulling out the tiny head? Would I be reading articles about how to ace a job interview on the day I was allowed to start collecting my pension?

I needed to get a grip, to sit up. Life was happening and it was leaving me behind.

People

As I was sulking Paddy ran into my room, wearing his Cinderella dress this time. He had something in his hand.

'Got you a present, Gracie,' he said, dropping something on the bed.

It was a little parcel of toilet paper with something soft and wet inside.

'What is it, Paddy?' I asked, not touching it.

'Apples!' he said, unwrapping the paper to show me the pale yellow mush inside. 'Chewed it, made it soft.'

'Great, thank you,' I said, making a face. 'Can you take it off my bed though, please? I don't want it to make the covers all wet.'

Paddy nodded earnestly. 'OK, Gracie.'

He scooped up the parcel and ran out of my room again.

Later that day, I recounted my underwhelming coming-out story to Til as we sat in Queen's Park.

'Everything's moving quickly, then,' she said, putting her hands behind her head and lying back on the grass.

'Not really,' I said. 'The opposite, in fact. I'm just trying to catch up now. Oh!' I said, suddenly thinking of something.

'I haven't let the internet know yet.'

'Will they be interested?' Til asked.

'Of course!' I said indignantly. 'People are interested if you have a nice biscuit. This will be big news.'

I opened my phone and found a video of 'I'm Coming Out' by Diana Ross on YouTube. I posted it to Twitter with the caption:

Just something I wanted to share with you all #sogay

Til opened her own phone and scrolled down to my update. 'Ha,' she said. 'Classy.' She lay back down. 'You like her then? The Welsh library girl?'

'Yeah,' I said, thoughtfully. 'I think I do. I mean, I definitely do, actually.'

'She *is* hot.' Til picked a daisy from the grass by her side and idly twirled it around in her fingers.

I grinned. 'I know, right. But I just like her, you know. Like, *like* her. She talks to me.'

'Well, it's a start, I guess,' Til said, her eyes still closed.

'Also,' I said, pushing myself upright and sitting cross-legged, looking down at Til. 'You know what's good? Meeting someone new. When do we ever meet new people? The only people I ever see are people from school, who I've known since I was four years old, for heaven's sake. There are six billion or whatever people on the planet and I only see the same tiny, boring selection over and over.'

'Oi,' Til said, punching me in the thigh without opening her eyes.

'OK, not all boring. But still.' I put my hand on Til's arm suddenly. 'Oh my god, Til, do you know what I think it is?'

'What?' she opened her eyes and squinted at me, holding her hand up to shield her face from the sun.

'I'm a people person! I've just realised. I like people! I just never get to meet any new ones!'

'Ha!' Til closed her eyes again and put her head back down on the grass. 'Shut up, Grace, you are not a people person.'

'I am, Til. I honestly think that's it. That's why I went so mad in my room, studying all the time. When you're a people person like I am, you need to meet new people to stay energised. I read about it once.'

'Right,' Til said.

From where I was sitting, I could see two people – a man and woman, probably in their early twenties – sitting in a patch of sunlight over towards the pond. The man was lying on a rainbow-coloured blanket. The woman was spinning a hula hoop around her arm.

'Oh my god, Til, it's *them*,' I said quietly.

'Who?' Til said, turning her head in the direction I was looking but not sitting up.

'Remember when I had my epiphany on the way back from the hospital? When I realised I was going to start living for the moment? It was those people who inspired me. It's like they were my . . . my muse. I saw them and I knew it was how I wanted to be. Free and happy and in the moment.'

Til sat up now and looked at them properly. 'They look drunk.'

'They don't.'

'Actually, they look insane.'

'They don't! They just look relaxed, like they don't have anything to worry about except being right here right now.'

'That's what insane people look like.'

Til lay back down and I carried on watching them as the woman started twirling the hoop around her waist.

'I'm going to go and talk to them,' I said.

Til didn't even open her eyes. 'You are not.'

'I am.' I got to my feet. 'Because I'm a people person. And they are definitely people.'

Making Friends

Til opened one eye to watch me as I made my way over to them.

I'd only taken about three steps when already I'd begun to change my mind. What in heaven's name was I going to say to these perfect strangers? If I'd been in the park alone I would have veered away, changed direction and headed for the ice-cream kiosk or the toilets or something. I wouldn't have seen it through. But Til was watching me and stubborn pride kept me on a steady course for where they were sitting.

I stopped a couple of metres away from them and fiddled with a piece of bark on a tree for no other reason than that it gave me something to do with my hands.

'Cool hooping,' I said casually.

Was that even what it was called? Or was it 'hula-ing'?

'Ah, thanks, babe,' the girl said, stopping the hoop and holding it steady around her middle.

She had an accent. Australian. I might have guessed. Everything about her seemed Australian. Even from a distance I could tell she probably grew up walking barefoot on sun-drenched beaches, surfing and barbecuing. Saying 'no dramas!' to anything and everything.

189

She stepped out of the hoop and held it out to me. 'You wanna go?'

My first instinct was to say no – old habits die hard, after all – but I stopped myself.

'Sure,' I said, taking the hoop and stepping into it, in the assured manner of someone who was very confident about their own abilities to propel a plastic ring around their middle with the force of their pelvic swing alone.

The only thing was, it turned out that hula-hooping is hard. The hoop spun once around my waist before dropping unceremoniously to the floor. I tried again, but managed even less than one full rotation that time.

I decided it was best to laugh it off. 'It's been a while!' I said, handing back the hoop. The girl gave me a supportive smile.

The boy, who was lying on the grass, leaning back on his elbows, held a bag of Doritos out to me. 'Crisps?' he said.

I had to bend down to reach one so I took the opportunity to transition seamlessly into a seated position. This was taking things up a level, I knew. Sitting down, sharing their little patch of park, without formal invitation. I felt very bold indeed. And also very aware of the potential for social awkwardness here. Would they clear their throats uncomfortably, and make some excuse about why I should move on now?

They didn't.

'I'm Spider,' the boy said, through a mouthful of crisps.

'I'm Grace.'

'Well, hey there, Grace,' the girl said, setting the hoop spinning around her again. 'I'm Vicky.'

That was that.

I couldn't get over how easy it all was. It seemed like all you had to do was have a look around for someone you thought might be interesting, sit down next to them and introduce yourself. So why on earth had I stuck so rigidly to the same social circle for so long?

After ten minutes or so, Til obviously realised I was making myself at home and she ambled over. 'I'm gonna head off then.'

'OK,' I shrugged. I could have asked her to join us but I knew she'd only sit there with her eyebrows halfway up her forehead making it quite clear she thought they were 'insane' or whatever it was she'd said. Anyway, I didn't have to do everything with Til, did I? She'd been pathetically central to my social life for too long. It was time to branch out!

'Bye then,' Til said, somewhat coldly.

'Bye!' I waved cheerfully.

My Idols

'So, you live around here, Grace?' Vicky said, leaning her hoop up against a tree and sitting down next to Spider.

'Up there,' I said, pointing vaguely towards the hill behind the park. 'You?'

Vicky laughed. 'We live everywhere!'

'Oh, OK,' I said, frowning slightly. This seemed an unusual answer to a straightforward question.

'We move around a lot,' Spider explained. 'We follow the sunshine. And the work. The seaside is best for both in the summer. Loads of tourists. So yeah, we live here, for now.'

'What work do you do?' I asked, then immediately cursed myself. 'What do you do for a living?' was such a boring, judgmental question.

They didn't seem worried though.

'Anything,' Spider said with a shrug and a smile. 'Bar work. Busking. He nodded towards a battered old acoustic guitar covered with black and white stickers. 'We just wake up and . . . take the day from there. If you know what I mean.'

'Wow,' I said, and I meant it. When I'd spotted these two

here in the park on my way home from the hospital, and randomly taken them as my inspiration, as my sign that I needed to stop waiting and start living, little did I realise how completely their lifestyle would encapsulate my ambitions. To just wake up and take the day from there! *That* was what I was talking about.

'What do you do with your time?' he asked.

I shrugged. It was a good question. I was only just working that out myself. 'I just finished my exams so I was doing that . . .'

'And now?'

I laughed and lay back on the grass. 'Whatever I feel like!' I hoped I was able to make this sound enigmatic enough to disguise the fact I couldn't think of anything substantial to say about my interests or passions or, in fact, personality.

'Cool,' Spider said. And he didn't press me any further.

Vicky reached into a rucksack and pulled out a four-pack of beer. 'You want one?' she said, holding one out to me.

'Sure.' I took it from her.

Why not?

Vicky snapped open her own can, took a long sip, then lay down on the grass, her head resting in Spider's lap. He stroked her hair, then he bent down and kissed her on the forehead once.

'You guys are together then?' I said casually, although inside I was wondering if the kiss was their way of letting me know I was a gooseberry, that I was crashing their date.

Neither of them said anything. Spider just grinned and took a slug of his beer.

I supposed that was a yes? Maybe they thought the question was rhetorical. Or just plain stupid. Clearly they were together.

I wasn't an accustomed drinker by any means. I'd had a can or two of Guinness with Til but that was it. I wasn't sure what this beer was – it tasted like what I assumed rust would taste like – but I liked the effect it was having on me. I was experiencing a sensation like being enveloped in a warm, peaceful fog.

'What's on your jacket?' Spider said, nodding towards it.

I looked down at the breast pocket on my denim jacket and saw a dark wet circle that was slowly growing. 'I don't know . . .' I reached inside. 'Ugh!' I said, as my fingers touched something soft and moist. I hitched it out. 'Oh, Paddy . . .' I muttered.

After I'd asked Paddy to remove his chewed apple offering from my bed, he'd obviously decided to tuck it into my pocket, perhaps in case I fancied a snack during the course of the day and lacked the energy to chew my own fruit.

'It's apple,' I explained. 'My little brother likes to give me weird presents.'

'Oh, right,' Spider said, looking a bit bemused but laughing.

And then I started laughing too. And then I found that I couldn't stop. I knew it wasn't that funny really but I was just overcome with it. I don't know if it was the beer or what, but it felt good. I wondered how long it was since I'd really, properly laughed.

Vicky lifted her head up and looked at me. 'Oh god,' she said, smiling. 'We've got a lightweight here.'

It was kindly, I felt, the way she spoke to me. She was smiling at me kindly. These people were kind. I'd come over, they'd welcomed me, given me delicious crisps and this wonderful magical can of alcohol and here I was laughing and laughing with them as if I'd known them all my life.

Wasn't summer amazing? Wasn't life amazing?

Time seemed to jump forward several hours in one go. The sun was slipping behind the trees and our patch of park became shady.

Suddenly Spider sat up and said, 'Let's go to the beach.'

Vicky said, 'Is Bobby there tonight?' without opening her eyes.

'Should be,' Spider said. Then he turned to me. 'Want to come to a party, Grace?'

'A party?' I said. My (limited) experience of parties hadn't been generally good. They normally involved being squashed into someone's parents' lounge with a random selection of people from school who I didn't want to talk to, looking at my watch and thinking of an excuse I could give as to why as I had to get away early.

'Our mate Bobby DJs outside Bar Ten. It's pretty chilled. Just drinks and fires and stuff. Not really a party. Just a gathering.'

Gathering. That was a code word I knew. Til had told me that that's just what people say when they're having a party and either a) they don't want their parents to be alarmed or b) they're trying to downplay it so if no one turns up they don't look stupid. It seemed unlikely that either of these scenarios applied here though. Maybe it *was* just a gathering. Some free-spirited people gathering on the beach to listen to music and sit by fires and be free spirits together.

I looked at my watch.

'You got something to get back for?' Vicky said. 'Parents?'

That settled it. I certainly wasn't going to drift away early, to make my excuses, just for an evening at home with my parents. I didn't want to be seen as that kind of person. I wasn't that kind of person! Not any more.

I was going to a party.

PART 5

During which I learn how to have FUN, for crying out loud

Gathering

I drank another can on the way to the beach and by the time we walked down the steps to the prom I felt a bit dizzy and very chatty.

A table was set up outside Bar Ten with two stacks of speakers on either side. A man wearing a red-and-white bandana and a black vest was fiddling with some dials on a set of decks on the table. He was holding a pair of headphones up to one side of his head and nodding along to the music. It was something thumpy and electronic that I didn't recognise, but I knew it must be terribly cool so I started to nod my head along too, and tap my hand against my thigh in the manner of someone truly appreciative of the craft. I figured this must be Bobby because when he saw Vicky and Spider he raised one hand in a wave.

There were little camps of people in front of the decks – groups of three or four or five sitting around in circles on the stones, some of them with disposable barbecues in the middle, some of them on blankets.

Vicky and Spider spotted some people they knew. Spider called over and waved, and I followed him over to them.

There were four or five people in the group. Some male, some female. My memory's a little hazy on the details. Vicky hugged each of them in turn, called them all 'babe!' (with an exclamation mark) and said things about it being so amazing to see them and how it had been way too long and weren't they all looking beautiful and happy. I realised then that everyone was sitting down except for me. I stood over them, swaying slightly.

'Sit down, girl!' Vicky said, laughing and pulling me down by the sleeve. 'Guys, this is Grace.'

The people all said hello and Vicky told me their names. I can't remember what they were exactly but it seemed to me that it was unlikely they were using the names that appeared on their birth certificates. They were all Rainbow, Pongo, Mango, Cheese – words like that.

They all blurred into one, really, the people – tanned skin, hair bleached by the sun, ragged, faded clothing that looked like it'd been worn for a cross-channel swim then beaten against a rock to dry. I sat amongst them and gazed around at their faces in wonder.

I'd never been with people like that before. People just sitting on the beach listening to music, just living. These people weren't checking the temperature on the washing machine to make sure Mum didn't shrink their best pyjamas. These people weren't trying to work out how many pages they could read about sedimentary rock formation before they had to move on to work through a list of 408 quadratic equations.

I listened to snippets of conversation without really joining in.

One woman seemed to be complaining about an ex-boyfriend she'd just dumped for spending too much time at work.

'He was always like, "I can't, baby. I'm on a call to America, I can't just leave." On a call to America! What a loser. He was speaking to a fat man called Dwayne who worked in a hut in a car park in Idaho, not conferencing with the White House.'

I laughed when everyone else laughed, and smiled when anyone looked at me. I didn't say anything.

'Yol-reet-tair-kit?' one man said to me suddenly.

I just looked at him. I was feeling so mellow and spaced out since my beers that I couldn't even work up the energy to say 'pardon'.

Yol-reet-tair-kit, I said in my head. Yol-reet-tair-kit. What did *that* mean? Was he speaking English? Was he offering me a drug I didn't know the name of?

After a few moments of this confused silence, the man laughed. 'I said: You. All right. There. Kid,' he said slowly and clearly. 'My accent a bi' much for ye, eh?'

I blinked. Everything seemed to be moving in slow motion.

'Your accent . . .' I said stupidly.

'Aye,' he said. 'Glasgow-born and bred. I'll try and tone it down for you.' Then he grinned. 'You English!'

I nodded and smiled back, like a mesmerised mute.

'So, are you?'

'Huh?' I said.

'Are you all right?'

'Yes!' I said. 'I'm wonderful! What's your name?'

The man laughed again. 'Tinks, remember? Vicks just told you.'

I frowned. 'Yes,' I said. 'That sounds right.'

'You like the music?' he asked.

I nodded.

'Don't say much, do you?'

'I do,' I said, sitting up straight and mentally pulling myself together. 'I say lots of things! All sorts of things. I have a lot to say for myself.'

Tinks laughed. 'I'm all ears,' he said.

I took that as a challenge of sorts, and I told Scottish Tinks all about my brush with a potentially fatal tropical disease and my resolution – inspired by my sighting of Vicky and Spider that same day – to live every day as if it was my last. I can't remember what Tinks said about my grand plan but I got the general impression he approved.

I can't remember what a lot of people said that evening, but people seemed to look at me with crinkles round their eyes. Laughing at me. Not unkindly, just like they found me amusing in some way.

Prophecy

I didn't stay with Vicky and Spider and our little gang of Pongo Mango Cheddar et cetera all night. I roamed around. I mingled!

I strolled around from group to group, taking it in turns to sit down with different ones. All of them tended to look at me with their heads on one side. All of them chuckled a bit. I told all of them about my epiphany, and recommended they follow the same plan. I was like a prophet! I just didn't want anyone to make the mistakes I had.

I told one girl about how long I had spent on my heat-transfer science project, going, inexplicably, into quite some detail. Even at the time I wasn't sure why I felt the need to furnish her with quite so much information. I just found myself saying, 'Heat energy moves by three methods, you see. Conduction, convection and radiation,' and there didn't seem to be any coming back from it by that point.

'Anyway,' I said as I realised people were starting to lose interest, to look in the opposite direction. 'AN. Y. WAY. The point is, I was wrong! Wrong to waste so much time. There is no future. There is no past. There is only today. There is only this second. Oh wait! That one's gone now! You see? Gone. Now there's only THIS one. This second. And now this one. See how fast they move? Seconds? You can't hold on to them! Don't even try!'

I realised I was shouting. The man I was talking to – I can't even guess what his name might have been – held his hands up. 'Woah, OK!' he said, laughing. 'I got it. No holding on to seconds. I won't even try.'

Just then I was distracted by the sight of two women. One of them was lying with her head in the other one's lap.

'I'm a lesbian, you know,' I said suddenly.

'Huh?' he said.

I nodded over to the women. 'I'm a lesbian too. I'm seeing this girl. Sarah. She's Welsh.'

The man looked over and made the link. 'Oh, they're not together,' he said. 'They're just drunk. Makes them touchy-feely.'

'Oh,' I said, squinting at them. 'Well, I'm a real one.'

'Cool,' he said.

'What's cool?' Vicky said, coming over to join us.

'I'm a lesbian,' I told her, starting to get used to the sound of it. 'I probably should've told you before.'

Vicky just laughed. 'Right you are, kiddo,' she said.

'It's not a secret,' I said.

'No, I can see,' she said. She and the man whose name I can't remember looked at each other and smiled.

'I'm not ashamed! I just like girls!' I said. I was shouting again. I didn't know why. 'Especially French ones, I think.'

Vicky laughed again and then suddenly she was leaning

towards me. I had no idea what was going on until her mouth was on mine. And then her tongue was in my mouth! I didn't know what to do with it. I just sat there, my face frozen. A couple of people around us said something like 'wahey!' but still I didn't move. Eventually, Vicky stopped licking round my face like a spaniel and she sat back up and laughed. I remember thinking how completely different kissing her felt to kissing Sarah. Sarah was soft and she smelt like washing powder and mint. Vicky tasted of cigarettes and her mouth seemed enormous, like she could swallow my whole head if she wanted.

I could see Spider, in the group next to us. I looked at him, waiting to see what his reaction would be to his girlfriend kissing me. He just rolled his eyes, took a swig from his can and turned back to his conversation.

I wasn't sure what to make of it. Was Vicky in love with me? I wasn't ready for all this. Maybe I was one of those people who just oozes charm and charisma and sex appeal? Someone who literally can't enter a room without people falling for them? Maybe people had secretly been wanting to pounce on me all my life but it was only now I was telling people I was officially a lesbian that they had the courage to go for it?

I sat still, my legs crossed, pondering this possibility. Vicky got up and strolled off, and sat down with another group.

'Vicksgottya, eh?'

I looked up. Scottish Tinks. 'Vick's got to you, has she?' he said again.

I didn't say anything.

'That girl is like a fiend for a snog. She likes the new ones best.'

I just blinked.

'Poor wee lassie,' Tinks said, laughing, and he too ambled off.

I realised then what an idiot I was being. This was just how these people rolled! This is how they did things. You want to kiss someone; you just kiss them. It doesn't mean anything. Nothing means anything in the end. You just do things in that moment, and then that moment's gone.

I got up, and staggered around for a bit. The stones had suddenly become very difficult to walk over without stumbling. A few people helped me back up when I had to lean on their shoulders for support.

I clambered off the pebbly beach and onto the prom, wondering if I could go inside the bar to find a toilet or if the bouncer would stop me on the door and ask for ID.

'Hey, Grace.'

I looked up. Sarah was sitting on the low wall between the bar and prom, her hands in her pockets.

She gave me a smile but her eyes were sad.

'Sarah . . .' I said stupidly.

'You've had a bit, then,' she said, and she laughed once, but still her eyes didn't smile.

'A bit . . . ?'

'To drink. You drunk?'

'No!' I said too loudly. 'Not drunk. Just, you know . . . I'm at a party and, you know . . .'

I was struggling to think of words. My brain felt full of cotton wool.

'That one seems to like you,' she said, nodding her head casually towards where Vicky was standing in a space on her own, dancing with her hands above her head, sloshing her can of beer all over a nearby group.

'She kissed me,' I said, more to myself than to Sarah, as if I was just reminding myself that it had happened.

'I know. I saw,' Sarah said.

Slowly, slowly, my brain started to catch up.

'Oh. But I went out to the gig with you and then we went to the beach and you kissed me and then you said "I like you" and now I'm on the beach again and I kissed Vicky.'

What had happened with Vicky seemed so completely different and unrelated to my evening on the beach with Sarah that I hadn't properly processed the idea that, from the outside, this might present a problem.

Sarah did the hard laugh again. 'Yeah. That's pretty much it.'

'You're angry,' I said.

Sarah shook her head. 'No, not at all. It was one date. I just thought we had a good time and I don't know, I don't really do . . . kissing on the beach every day, you know? I didn't realise that you did, that was all.'

I didn't realise that I did either. But apparently I did. That's what I did now.

'Hey, Gracie,' Vicky called suddenly. 'Come and dance with us!'

I turned around to see where her voice was coming from, and when I turned back to Sarah, she'd stood up.

'Have fun,' she said, taking her phone out of her pocket and typing into it, no longer giving me her full attention.

'Yeah,' I said, which didn't even make sense but I was too drunk to piece together anything more meaningful. She ambled off. I wanted to call after her, but by the time I'd thought about it she was too far away to hear.

I watched her walk for a while, wondering where she was going. To revise, perhaps. To learn some science. Or to go to bed early to get up for her library shift. Was that why I liked her? Or, why I thought I liked her? She was everything I used to be. Sensible. Planning for the future. But I had to let that go. That wasn't me any more. Sarah was a good match for the old Grace, not the new one.

'GRAACIIIE!' Vicky called again. I stumbled over the stones to join her, just in time to see her projectile vomit into the glowing embers of a disposable barbecue, sending up a plume of noxious steam.

Oversharing

The morning after the beach party I had my first ever hangover, although of course, I had no way of recognising it as such.

My first thought was Sarah.

Oh god, why?

Why hadn't I pushed Vicky away? Why hadn't I better explained the whole thing to Sarah? Why hadn't I gone after her?

I reached for my phone and tried to compose a message. I really wanted to say sorry, but it was hard to know exactly what for. If I apologised too much for letting Vicky kiss me, then Sarah might think I was getting ahead of myself, assuming I was more important to her than I was. I decided it was best to keep things vague:

Sorry about last night.
Too much to drink.

As soon as I sent it I wished I'd said something else. Explained myself better. Made a joke. Added a kiss, or even a smiley face.

I sighed and turned over, then I read through all the tweets and Instagram comments I'd posted during the beach party. I had barely any recollection of writing any of them.

Some of them were innocent enough:

Literally nothing better than Brighton beach in the summer.

Some made me cringe a bit:

That thing where you go to a party and every single person there is awesome.

Some were borderline racist:

Scottish people need to learn to speak English!

And there were some where I had no way of knowing whether I had actually typed out the words or if I had just sat on my phone:

Wahhhe JJJJJ YES Why not

I had also, I noticed, posted a link to an article. I vaguely remembered doing it – I'd been waiting in the queue for the toilet and idly browsing the internet and had found a page that listed out every festival in the UK that summer, with prices, line-ups and camping details. I'd tweeted the link with the comment 'This is useful'.

This had been quite a deliberate move, I remembered. I was quite clearly sending a message that Grace Dart was the kind of person who went to festivals. In fact, she was the kind of person who went to so many festivals that she needed access to a one-stop-shop checklist just to make sure she was able to keep a handle on all the festivity.

The replies I'd received were strange though:

Ew gross.

Ouch!

U OK?

I looked back at my original tweet and clicked the link I'd posted. I was then that I realised that, horror beyond horror, the information I had somehow shared with my followers wasn't in fact a handy list of summer festivals but a medical article entitled 'Do I have herpes and what should I do about it?'

Somehow, during my post-hospital research into herpes simplex, I'd managed to save the link. And now, I had somehow managed to share it.

I knew there was no point posting extended updates explaining to my followers, as nurse Claudette had done to me, that it wasn't necessarily a sex disease and that a cold sore was a perfectly innocent, common complaint. Instead, I just quietly deleted the tweet. Although I knew that, as is the way with these things, the damage was already done.

Like Disgusting

I heard Paddy driving his remote-control car into my bedroom door repeatedly before he eventually burst through. He was completely naked apart from my school tie, which he'd tied around his head.

He jumped onto my bed and pushed his forehead against mine. 'Ugh!' he said, backing away and covering his whole face with his hand. 'You stink like disgusting, Gracie.'

I felt like disgusting.

'Get Mum,' I said to him. 'Tell her I'm seriously ill.'

Paddy's eyes widened and he jumped off the bed.

'Muuuuuuum!' he shouted from the top of the stairs. 'Grace is Sicily ill!'

A few moments later, Mum came into the bedroom. She was carrying a glass of water. She took something white out of a little blue sachet and dropped it into the glass. It fizzed violently as she handed it to me.

'Oh dear,' she said, shaking her head. 'Overdid it, did we?'

'What's that?' I said, taking the glass and watching the little white lozenge dart around like something from a science experiment.

Ollie came in to join the party, and he, Mum and Paddy stood in a row at the end of my bed. Ollie and Mum both had their arms folded. When Paddy realised this, he copied the pose and shook his head in disappointment at me.

'Oh dear,' Ollie said.

'Oh dear,' Paddy echoed.

'You know you've got it bad when you have to drink that.' Ollie nodded towards the glass. 'Looks and taste like spit. The only thing to make you feel worse than you do now, I guarantee it.'

'It will make her feel better!' Mum protested.

Ollie shook his head. 'Nah. No way. You always say that but it's a lie. Maybe hangovers in the eighties or whatever were different.'

'I don't want it,' I said, putting the glass down next to my bed. 'I cannot even begin to entertain the idea of putting anything in my mouth. All please leave now.'

'You were the one who summoned me!' Mum pointed out.

'Well, now you are dismissed.' I lay back on my pillow and put the duvet over my head. 'Well done, family,' I said, my voice muffled by the covers. 'Thank you for your invaluable support.'

I had a lot of Twitter and Instagram comments since yesterday's drunken update spree and many of my followers were speculating about the intensity of my hangover this morning. I decided to give the people what they wanted and live-tweeted my delicate emotional and physical state for a while to distract myself from the fact that Sarah still hadn't replied.

I kept alternating between feeling too hot and too cold and I just couldn't get comfortable. In the end I got desperate enough to sample the spit-flavoured drink.

Ollie was right. It was repulsive. I took two mouthfuls before I felt myself gagging. Then I decided to get up and have a shower.

When I came downstairs fifteen minutes later, I felt marginally better, but still not healthy by any means.

'It's a lovely day,' Mum said. 'I've made you a ham and coleslaw sandwich. Go and sit in the park and let the alcohol evaporate from your pores.'

'I don't want to sit in the park with a ham and coleslaw sandwich. I want to sit very still in a darkened room and contemplate my unfortunate situation.'

'Either you go out, or you stay here and help me with him.' Mum nodded towards Paddy.

He was trying to get Dick the giraffe to stand upright on the back of the sofa, but Dick's floppy stuffed legs meant he kept tumbling forward.

'Dick,' Paddy said seriously. 'I do not have time for this.' Then he turned and shouted, 'Mum! Make Dick stop being so floppy!'

'Paddy, stop shouting, for god's sake!' Dad yelled from the top of the stairs before returning to his bedroom and slamming the door.

I looked at Mum. Dad wasn't really the snapping kind. 'What's up with Dad?'

Mum frowned and looked upwards towards their bedroom. 'He's been in a bad mood lately. I think it's your nan. He's still sad. Will be for a while, I should think.'

I nodded and looked down. I felt guilty. Of course he was. That should have been obvious.

'OK,' I sighed. 'I'm going out then.'

Strangers

Lying in the sun in the park I felt so exhausted and broken that I dozed off, right there on the grass.

When I came round, I anxiously fumbled for my phone. I was sure that Sarah would have replied. Even if she was at work, she must've had a break by now.

There was nothing.

I realised that it was quite likely she never would. What did I expect her to say? I wished I'd asked her a direct question, something that she could only ignore if she wanted to send me a very clear signal not to bother her. As it was, I wasn't sure what it meant.

I groggily contemplated what I could do that day to continue my philosophy of spontaneous living. I decided that I wasn't really in the best state for seizing the day. It would take all my concentration just to survive it.

I took my phone out of my pocket and texted Til.

I'm in the park, dying a slow and painful alcohol-related death. Come down.

When Til arrived half an hour later, she had with her a text-book called *Understanding Plumbing and Heating Systems*.

'Looks fascinating,' I commented, with one eye open.

'It's all right, actually,' she said. 'I want to be prepared. It's not that long till we go back.'

I made a face. 'It's ages yet.'

'Not really,' she said. 'A few weeks. Haven't you got any reading to do? I bet there's a ton of pre-work for the kinds of A levels you've signed yourself up for.'

'I don't want to talk about it,' I said, and I really didn't. 'Stop going on about it, will you?'

'I wasn't,' Til said with a shrug. Then she nodded over to the corner of the park. 'Look. There are your mates.' I noted a tone of disdain in the way she said 'mates'.

I looked to where she was pointing and saw Vicky and Spider in the same place they'd been the day before, sitting cross-legged on their rainbow blanket, playing cards.

'Oh yeah,' I said, pushing myself upright. 'Come and meet them.'

'Fine.' Til sighed and closed her textbook and we went over.

'Hey,' I said as we approached.

'Oh hey, babe!' Vicky said with a wave.

I was surprised to see they both had open cans of beer next to them. I could barely look at one without feeling ill. I supposed they were more seasoned partiers than I was. Which wouldn't exactly have been hard.

'This is my friend Til,' I said.

Til nodded and managed only the coolest of smiles. 'All right?'

'You want to play?' Spider said.

We nodded and he dealt us into the game, but after a couple of hands I had to announce my retirement due to my pounding head.

Til said, 'Yeah, I'm done too. I'm going to go home and unscrew a U-bend.'

'She's training to be a plumber,' I explained.

Vicky screwed up her nose. 'God. No way I could handle putting my hand down other people's manky dunnies all day. Rather you than me, babe!'

Til rolled her eyes. 'Yeah. Anyway. Bye.'

She got up and headed towards the park's main exit.

Vicky pulled a face. 'God. She's a bit uptight, hey?'

I just shrugged. Til didn't look back as she reached the gate and let herself out of the park and into the road.

'You have a good time last night?' Spider asked.

I nodded slowly. 'I think so.'

Spider laughed. 'You were making lots of new friends. I think you told everyone on that beach about how important it is to seize the day.'

I groaned. 'Sorry,' I said. 'Idiot.'

Spider shook his head. 'Nah. You were fine. People liked you! So what's the story anyway? You doing some kind of bucket-list challenge?'

I shook my head. 'Not really. It's not as organised as that. I'm just trying not to waste time. Not to waste any days.'

As I was saying this, it occurred to me that maybe a list

wasn't a bad idea. I had been using 'My Ultimate Bucket List' for inspiration, but if there was one thing I knew for sure it was that time was short. Maybe a list would help me make sure I didn't miss off anything vital?

Spider thought for a moment. 'Is it like that saying "Do one thing every day that scares you"?'

'I don't know. Not quite, I don't think. I don't really like being scared. I'm not aiming for fear. I went on this massive swing thing the other day but I didn't like it that much. It wasn't the best thing I've done, anyway, since I started the plan.'

'What was the best thing?' Spider asked.

I thought about this for a moment and realised the answer was obvious. 'I went to Paris,' I said. 'With my nan. And it was OK. I mean, it was good. Random and weird but good. But then she died, right after.'

'You killed your nan?' Vicky said loudly, lifting her head up.

Spider gave her a sharp look and she mumbled, 'Sorry,' and lay back down.

'No,' I said. 'It turned out she was ill but that trip was the last time . . .'

I couldn't finish the explanation. I was getting too choked up. It was partly the hangover perhaps, but really just the image of Nan, sitting outside that cafe with her red wine, posing with the crazy grin outside the butcher's.

Spider put his hand on my knee and gave me a kind smile.

Vicky sat up and pulled me into a hug. 'Ah, babe. Don't blub.' She smelt faintly of beer and sweat. I hoped she wouldn't try to kiss me again.

'What are you going to do today, then?' Spider asked, clearly trying to brighten the tone of the conversation. 'How are you seizing today?'

I lay down on the floor and spread out my arms and legs like a starfish. 'I don't know. I guess I'll just have to see what comes to me.'

'You want to come back to ours?' Vicky said suddenly.

For some reason I felt the need to look at her to check she was talking to me, even though I don't know who else she could've been talking to.

'Hey, maybe that can be your thing for today!' she said. 'Going back to our flat. Who knows what you'll find there! Who knows what we'll do to you! It's a real adventure!'

The Flat

I did go back with them.

The flat was a one-bedroom top-floor flat in one of the old buildings on the roads that lead from the main high street down to the seafront, on the border of Brighton and Hove. It was just two rooms really – a bedroom and an all-in-one lounge and kitchen room with a red sofa pushed against one wall and a TV on a table in the corner. It was painted white but the walls were covered with paintings. They weren't in frames, they were just big sheets of A3 paper, Blu-Tacked straight onto the paintwork.

'Vicky's art,' Spider said when he saw me looking. 'Talented, isn't she?'

I nodded as was the polite thing to do – and I could see that, technically speaking, they probably were quite good – but the paintings made me nervous.

They featured disembodied heads and creepy children screaming in the dark and dolls with black holes for eyes and all sorts of other horrors. I wasn't sure I'd have felt too comfortable with that lot staring down at me when I was trying to spend a quiet evening in front of the telly.

'It's a nice flat,' I said, leaning on the windowsill and sticking my head out of the window. If you looked to the left you could just about make out the sea at the end of the road. Seagulls called above me and I could smell the barbecues from the lawns in front of the beach.

'It's my uncle's,' Spider said, coming to stand next to me. 'He lives in London but he uses it at the weekend. Or he used to. He's sick now. Too sick to get down here.'

Spider pushed his hands in his pockets and looked out of the window sadly.

'Lucky for us!' Vicky called from the sofa, where she was sitting with her feet on the arm, painting her toenails. Spider's face moved into a small frown but he didn't say anything.

'I'm hungry,' Spider said, moving away from the window. 'You want chips?'

I nodded and Spider emptied an entire bag of frozen chips into a roasting tray and slid it into the oven. When they were ready, we sat cross-legged on the floor and ate them out of a giant mixing bowl while we played Monopoly.

The Way They Did Things

I liked Vicky and Spider. I liked their company and the way they did things.

They enthusiastically embraced my seize-the-day philosophy, and together we drew up a formal list of adventures and wrote it out on the chalkboard in the kitchen of the flat. These adventures ranged from simple, easily achievable pleasures like 'try a battered Mars Bar' or 'wear a bikini in the rain', to the more ambitious 'hula on the Great Wall of China' and 'busk outside the Taj Mahal'.

Sometimes, when we were talking, one of us might say something like, 'oh, I've never actually tasted real lobster' or 'kite-surfing looks cool' and another of us would get up and add it to the chalkboard. Even doing that felt good – the simple act of writing it down. Whereas other people might mention an idle interest then forget all about it, too bogged down in daily drudgery to ever revisit the idea, we kept a log of them. We had a plan of action. We were going to make things happen, somehow.

But despite our ever-growing list of experiences and

adventures we planned to have, the atmosphere at Vicky and Spider's was always one of relaxation.

Over the next week or so, I saw them almost every day. They even gave me a key so I could come and go without Spider having to come down the stairs to let me in. I would walk through town and along Western Road with my headphones on, dodging tourists and students and old people on mobility scooters. I felt free. I didn't have any plans. No one expected me to be anywhere. No one expected me to be anything.

They ate whatever was in the flat – frozen pizzas, biscuits, crackers – or noodles from foil trays from the Chinese takeaway opposite. They drank cans of beer from the fridge and water flavoured with lemon slices from the freezer. They listened to dance music on a tiny silver stereo or played their acoustic guitar. Sometimes Vicky would cover the kitchen floor with newspaper and work on a painting – big brushes, big strokes, huge tubs of paint sloshing all over herself and the flat. They didn't ask me many questions. They just seemed to accept that I was there.

Sometimes one of us would wander into the kitchen to peruse our list and call out a suggestion to the others. 'You know, if we really want to hold a husky puppy we could just go down to the dog's home and see one there', or 'Let's fly a kite today. We can get one from that shop on North Street and get a bus up to the Downs. It's definitely windy enough.'

If we did manage to do something, when we got back

to the flat we'd draw a thick chalk line through it, but we never rubbed anything off. I loved looking at those, the completed items. They reminded me just how much living I was doing these days.

While You Can

After a few weeks of hanging around with Vicky and Spider, I was helping Mum sort the clean laundry into piles on her bed and she asked me where I'd been going recently.

I shrugged. 'Just seeing friends,' I said.

'Til?' Mum asked.

'Sometimes.'

'Anyone else? Girls? Anyone special?'

I rolled my eyes. 'No, Mum. Nothing like that.'

'OK,' she said. 'Just asking. You're out a lot, that's all.'

I shrugged again. 'It's the summer holidays, isn't it. It's just nice not to have to revise all the time.'

Mum nodded. 'Fair enough. You thought about asking for your old job back, now school's over?'

I sighed. 'Can't I be allowed to have fun for a bit?'

'Of course, love,' Mum said calmly. 'I just thought a bit of extra cash might come in handy. Actually, they're looking for cover down at the clinic now that Lacey's off on maternity. I could put your name forward if you like. That'd be fun, wouldn't it? You and me working together?'

I made a face. 'No, Mother, that would not be fun. I don't

want to sit in a room full of people scratching their crotches, listening to you say words like 'discharge' and 'scrotum' on the phone all day. That would be abominable.'

Mum sighed. 'Oh, right. My mistake.'

Til made it quite clear that she thought it was strange that I was spending so much time with 'those weirdo hippies' so I simply stopped telling her when I was going to see them.

I still saw her a reasonable amount – every couple of days or so – but she seemed to be becoming more and more preoccupied with her upcoming college course. Whenever I went to her flat, she was lying on her floor with her textbook in front of her and collection of oddly shaped pieces of plastic spread out on the carpet.

Unlike me, Til did have a summer job. She was working nearly thirty hours a week in a shop on Western Road that sold second-hand phones, laptops and games consoles. Sometimes I'd call in to see her on my way to Vicky and Spider's, and on one of these occasions I made some idle comment about how she was going to regret wasting the whole summer either at work or lying on her bedroom floor looking at dismantled pipework. The comment did not go down well.

'Jesus, Grace. Listen to yourself. We don't all live in your little bubble, you know. We can't all spend every day lounging around in the park or on the beach with Mummy and Daddy pushing cash into our pockets. Mum's been off work for a week now. We're two hundred quid down on what we should be. I have to buy food with the money I make here. It's called survival, you know? And I'm sorry if plumbing isn't an exciting enough job for you and your new mates, but guess what? I want to actually be able to do something useful when I get out of college. I want to be able to do something that people will pay me real money for.'

I was taken aback. Til was moody and grumpy almost all of the time, but she was rarely angry. She never lost her temper.

I suddenly realised that maybe we weren't as good friends as I had thought. It had been OK when we were seeing each other every day at school, when we had lessons and the people around us in common. But now, without those ties, we were growing apart. I could see why she was annoyed at me; I didn't blame her for that. But the facts remained: maybe we were just too different now.

I mumbled an apology.

'I'm just trying to enjoy myself for a bit,' I said quietly. 'I don't want to ever think about study or work ever again.'

'Yeah, well,' Til said, her voice calmer again now. 'Enjoy it while you can. With the A levels you've chosen you won't have much time to enjoy anything come September.'

She was right, I knew, and the thought made me sick.

I was down to do four A levels. I'd had to get special permission to do that many. On top of the ones I'd always planned to do – English, history and biology – I'd decided to add art in case any future profession required me to demonstrate that I have a creative side. As it happened, I enjoyed art a lot, but I would never have factored something as frivolous as that into my decision.

'You're going to be busy,' Mrs Maybury, Head of Sixth Form, had warned.

'I know,' I'd said, and smiled. I'd felt smug! What an absolute fool I was.

Now, I was just pretending that it wasn't happening. That it was never *going* to happen. I was fooling myself into thinking that August was going to last forever, that it wouldn't morph slowly but surely into September, into September the sixth, the day when I'd have to go back to school and once again begin spending every day going from book to essay to book, from classroom to library to bedroom, trying to memorise facts I didn't want to know and write convincing essays exploring questions I didn't care about.

I was in denial, basically. And I think this was one of the main reasons I spent so much time with Vicky and Spider. They hadn't known me how I was before – when I was all revision cards and colour-coded Post-its and study schedules divided into twenty-minute chunks. When I'd turned down every invite that came my way to stay in my bedroom with a textbook.

When I'd walk disapprovingly past people getting drunk in the park, feeling sure that they were the ones throwing their lives away, and that I was the one with the right idea.

With Vicky and Spider, I could be whoever I wanted to be. I could reinvent myself. They didn't ask me what my plans for the future were. They didn't ask me about next year or even next week.

The most difficult question they ever asked me was if I wanted a cheese toastie or if I'd rather finish the potato waffles.

The List

Of course, it was only to be expected that the less effort required for an experience, the sooner we'd manage to get to it. The sooner it would be crossed off the list.

It took just ten minutes to assemble a steel band out of saucepans. We hired boards from the shop at the end of the road and were able to go body-boarding and be back at the flat for beers and noodles within the hour. Food-based experiences were particularly hassle-free so we embraced these with gusto: we made ice cream. We cooked a whole squid. We dipped crisps in melted chocolate.

Sometimes we added things to the list after we'd done them, just for the satisfaction of crossing them off. This is because there were occasions where we didn't realise we wanted to do something until we were halfway through doing it – like the time we decided to dye mashed potato pink with red food colouring – but that seemed no reason not to count it. Our list had got so long we'd had to extend it with big sheets of Vicky's painting paper. I liked adding things, even if it was only to cross them off immediately. It didn't lessen the sense of accomplishment.

I think Vicky and Spider felt the same, because on more than one occasion I noticed some corner-cutting. 'Learn to juggle with clubs' was proudly crossed off after a few feeble attempts down on the beach, even though neither Vicky nor I managed to successfully handle more than two clubs at once. One time, after a few cans of beer, I got misty-eyed and gave Vicky and Spider an impassioned case for why I wanted to do something for others.

I'd wobbled over to the kitchen and added 'Help a fellow person' to the bottom of the list.

'Bring us a beer then,' Vicky had called. 'If you really want to help a person out.'

I did as I was told, and when Vicky had finished her can, she'd got up and crossed my addition off the list.

'That's more than enough helping for one lifetime,' she told me.

Good Night

One morning I arrived at the flat to find Spider and Vicky fast asleep in bed and the lounge a complete mess – beer cans, pizza boxes and, for some reason, loose plastic daffodils were strewn over the carpet. There was an overflowing ashtray on the windowsill and the cushions had been pulled off the sofa and piled next to the television. They'd obviously had a party of some sort and judging by the degree of devastation it had been a good one. While I waited for them to stir, I took a photo of the scene and tweeted it with the caption:

You know it's been a good night when you wake up to this.

As I read the replies, I quickly realised that my followers had interpreted my comment to mean that I had been part of this wild evening myself, rather than just encountering it cold the next day. I didn't do anything to correct them.

I liked it, this impression I was creating of myself, as someone on a non-stop party rollercoaster. So what if that impression was a little contrived? Who cared if the persona was based on a curation of true and less-true events? Didn't we all spend basically our whole lives carefully manufacturing the impression we wanted to create of ourselves anyway? That was why we wore clothes, after all, or got our hair cut.

That was why we went to school on Mondays and told people we'd had a brilliant weekend when really we'd just watched *Masterchef* with Mum and Dad and made sure all our socks were in matching pairs.

Vicky

Out of the two of them – out of Vicky and Spider – Vicky was clearly in charge. She made the decisions. Spider might suggest something – a trip to the beach, that we clean the kitchen because ants were sticking to the orange juice we'd spilt on the side three days ago – but if Vicky didn't want to do it, it wouldn't happen.

I'd made a joke about this to Spider once when Vicky was out, and he'd given me a shy smile and looked down.

'Yeah,' he nodded, blowing a smoke ring out of the window. 'She calls the shots. She can be full-on. And yeah, she can do my head in sometimes, but . . . she rescued me, in a way.'

'Rescued you? From what?'

'From myself, I suppose. From boredom. From chronic inertia. I was living at home with my dad. He always wanted – always assumed – that I'd go into the family business, so I just kind of did. Seemed rude not to, and I didn't know what else I wanted to do anyway. So I'd go in every day and ring up a list of people who hadn't paid for their conservatories and send emails to builders and eat the same cheese-and-onion sandwich from the petrol station outside the office five days a week and then go home and watch rubbish TV and drink beer with my dad. Every day, always the same. Since Vicky came into my life – bulldozed into my life – every day's been different. I've done more stuff in the last year than in the rest of my life put together, you know?'

I nodded. I did know. Maybe people like me and Spider needed people like Vicky to spur us into action, to shake us up.

Sometimes, late in the evening, we'd watch films and Spider would blow smoke rings from the cigarettes he rolled and Vicky would drink cans of beer and then, usually near the end of the film, she would lean over and kiss me. It wasn't like that first time on the beach – like a big, wet eel flapping around in my face. I wasn't sure it was romantic kissing at all, but it was kissing. Proper on-the-mouth kissing.

I usually just sat there afterwards, wondering what I was supposed to do about it. I'd look at Spider, waiting for him to object, but he never even looked up. Then Vicky would move away from me, put her head on Spider's shoulder, and he'd drape his arm around her. I'd just go back to watching the film, act like I was completely at home with these kinds of impromptu displays of affection – if affection is what it even was – but they'd always leave me feeling strange. Was Vicky trying to tell me something? Should I ask her about it? Was there something going on I didn't know about?

I wasn't sure if I liked it or not. I liked that she wanted to do it, I decided. It was flattering, good for the ego. But

235

I didn't think I liked the actual process that much. Vicky tended to ambush me when I wasn't expecting it, when I was just trying to watch the telly or open a Pop Tart wrapper with my teeth. And also she smoked and drank a lot, so she always tasted slightly stale. But my lack of enthusiasm for this girl-on-girl action so soon after my official coming out alarmed me.

Maybe I wasn't a lesbian after all? I'd only just come out. Would I have to go back in again? Would Mum and Dad be disappointed? Mum had already told Hilary from Pilates, after all. But then I reminded myself of the statistics. Amelia. Elodie. Hot Miss Perrin. Sarah (Sarah was still very much on my mind). Girls 4, boys nil. It was still fairly conclusive, I decided.

Once, bold from beer, I plucked up the courage to address the kissing habit with Vicky. Specifically, to ask her why she did it.

She laughed. 'Why not? Maybe you just taste good, you little cutey.'

I didn't know what to make of this not-quite-an-answer.

It was true, I was quite heavy-handed with my application of mint-choc-chip lip balm, so maybe that's all there was to it.

Next time I went over, I picked up a Mint Whisper en route to give to Vicky. I hoped that might satisfy her mint-chocolate craving and she wouldn't feel the need to lick my face to get her fix.

It seemed altogether more hygienic that way.

Enjoyment

On my home for dinner one evening, I bumped into Sarah.

Instantly I felt my cheeks go pink. It was partly because I was surprised to see her, although I quickly realised I had no reason to be as my feet had automatically carried me on a route home that passed directly behind the library.

'Hi, Grace,' she said, looking up from fiddling with her bike lock.

'Hey!' My voice came out too brightly. I was overcompensating for the tension there'd been the last time we'd spoken, when she'd seen me drunkenly kissing an equally drunk Vicky that night at the beach gathering. 'How are you?'

She nodded. 'Yeah. Fine. How are you?'

I shrugged. 'Yeah. OK. You? Oh, sorry. We already did you, didn't we.'

Sarah laughed, then there was an awkward silence.

'I messaged you,' I said. And you didn't reply, I thought, but didn't say.

'Yeah.' She looked down at her bike and adjusted the position of the saddle slightly. Then there was silence again.

'So how goes the summer?' she said. 'You still fitting in lots of crazy stunts?'

I put my head on one side. 'Not crazy, really. But I've been doing some stuff, yeah. I went body-boarding. I ate frogs' legs.'

Sarah nodded. She pushed her jacket into the bag on the back of her bike. 'Any good?'

I wasn't sure which she was referring to so I answered for both. 'Body-boarding was cold. Frogs' legs were kind of disgusting.'

Sarah laughed again. 'Fair enough. Been doing anything you actually enjoy, then?'

'Yeah I . . .' I couldn't think of anything, not right there off the top of my head. I mean, I knew I had been having a great summer, I just couldn't think of a specific activity to mention right at that moment.

Sarah looked at me strangely. 'You know, Grace, you probably shouldn't seize the day by filling it with stuff you don't even like doing.'

'I'm not,' I protested. 'I've done loads of good stuff!'

Sarah smiled. 'OK!' she said brightly. 'Good.'

Then she climbed onto her bike and she was gone, and once again I was left wishing that I'd said something more, although I wasn't sure what.

I thought about what Sarah said as I continued on my way home. I was doing stuff, I enjoyed, wasn't I?

But then it was hard to always know, wasn't it, what was actually enjoyable and what wasn't. And should we only do the things we *know* we like? What about pushing ourselves? What about stepping outside of our comfort zones?

238

I suppose what I enjoyed the most when I was actually doing it was eating margarita pizza and watching the same box sets on repeat, but that wasn't the kind of thing you could look back on and feel proud of. And yes, maybe body-boarding and frogs' legs hadn't been episodes of unmitigated joy, but I was still glad I'd done them. I enjoyed the feeling of having done them. I enjoyed the feeling of telling people I'd done them.

That counted too, surely?

Help a Fellow Person

I don't know why I ended up reading the notice in the window of the Age Awareness UK shop at all, but something about it obviously caught my eye.

Volunteers wanted
to help clients in our drop-in IT centre.
Some computer skills a bonus.

I was interested that computer skills were only regarded as a 'bonus' attribute for this role. I wondered how far they'd get with someone who'd never so much as used a ticket machine at the station trying to help the old folk with their online banking.

Perhaps it was my conversation with Sarah that spurred me on – perhaps it had made me want to do something that I'd added to the list myself ('help a fellow person') rather than always going along with Vicky and Spider's choices – or if these weeks of seeking new experiences had just changed my default setting to one of doing things, as opposed to walking past on the other side of the road, but I found myself pushing open the door of Age Awareness

UK and approaching the woman at the counter.

'I can help,' I said brightly. 'Help people with computers, I mean. I'm OK at them. I can do the basics, anyway. Maybe a bit more than the basics, actually.'

She looked at me blankly.

'The sign,' I pointed to it. 'In the window?'

She squinted, looking over. 'Oh, yeah. I got you. Speak to Linda.' She nodded towards an archway at the back of the shop. Through the gap I could see a room with two rows of fairly shabby-looking desktop computers, arranged across long desks.

I went through the archway and into the room. All across the walls were posters featuring photos of smart, modern computers – much smarter and more modern than the ones in the room – being used by tanned, healthy-looking white-haired people in brightly coloured polo shirts. All of the people in the posters seem to be besides themselves with joy at whatever they were looking at on their screens.

The real people using the real computers in the actual room seemed less pleased. There was a woman with her hair in a bun typing furiously in the corner and a man with neatly combed hair and a green jumper frowning confusedly at a piece of paper in his lap.

Another much younger woman was crouching down, wrestling with a paper jam in a printer on the floor.

'Um . . . are you Linda?' I called to her from the archway.

'That's me,' she said with a sigh. She didn't look up.

'The other lady said I should talk to you about helping out in the IT centre.' I supposed this was the IT centre? 'I mean, helping out here.'

'Right you are,' Linda said, pushing herself up to a standing position with great effort. 'Put your name on the form and we'll be in touch.'

I was slightly put out by this unenthusiastic reaction to the generous offer of my time and expertise, but undeterred, I went over to the clipboard she'd pointed at, which was tied to a desk in the far corner. It was a simple blank table with spaces for names and email addresses. At the top it said, 'Volunteering expression of interest: complete your details below and we'll be in touch when a place on our training scheme becomes available.'

I scrunched up my nose. I didn't like the sound of this training scheme. I didn't like the sound of this waiting for a place. I wasn't looking for a full-time job. I didn't want to get roped into something serious. I just thought I'd pop in, show a few old folk how to check their emails for half an hour, then be on my way. This all seemed a bit much. I wanted to help people, sure, but I didn't want to put myself out too much to do it.

I was about to slink away, to continue on my way home, when the man with the green jumper and the neat hair turned around and looked at me nervously.

'Excuse me for bothering you . . . you couldn't give me a helping hand, could you?'

William

His voice started off loud, grew quiet in the middle, then loud again at the end, like he had no internal volume-adjustment mechanism.

'Um . . . sure.' I nodded and approached his workstation. 'I can try?'

His computer was open on the email account wjhellman@gmail.com. In front of him, there were several loose sheets of lined paper, obviously torn out of a notebook of some sort. They were filled with neat blue handwriting. At the top of each one there was a title:

Jerry

Dawn and Matthew

Abigail and boys

Council

'What it is,' he said, 'is I'm just trying to send a few notes to people – friends and family and what-have-you, but – it's silly, I know – I can't remember where to put the destination. The address?'

'The email address?'

He nodded enthusiastically. 'Exactly that.'

'Oh, OK,' I said. 'It's just here.' I pointed to his screen. 'This bar at the top where it says "to".'

The man squinted at the screen. 'Ah yes, right you are. It's coming back to me now. Jolly good. So, now then . . .' He shuffled his papers. 'This one is the email address, is it?'

He showed me something written below the name 'Jerry'. It looked like a plausible enough email address to me.

I nodded. 'Probably. You need to look for the 'at' symbol.'

'At . . .'

'It's the kind of 'a' sign in a circle.'

The man nodded again, firmly this time, but I could tell his confidence was feigned. 'Yep. Yes. I've got it. OK then, so it's J . . . where's the J? Oh, there it is! E . . . E . . . has this keyboard got an E? I don't think it has?'

'There,' I said, pointing to the E key on the keyboard. Admittedly the text was a little rubbed off.

'Ah!' he smiled. 'Got it.' He looked back up at the screen. 'Oh, where it's gone?'

His address bar was once again empty, his hard-won J and E nowhere to be seen.

'Um, I think you must've hit delete. Or maybe the cursor jumped or something . . .'

'Cursor . . .' he said slowly, turning the words over in his mouth. 'Cursor?'

'I could type it for you?' I found myself saying. It seemed beyond heartless not to offer. At this rate – of approximately one letter per two minutes – it would be Christmas before he'd sent his first email.

The man looked at me, amazed. Like I'd told him I could

converse fluently with badgers if he so required. 'Could you? Could you really do that?'

I nodded. 'Sure.'

He got up hurriedly as if he was anxious I would change my mind if he didn't make way for me immediately. I took my seat in the chair and entered Jerry's email address in the box.

'They've been on at me, you see,' the man said, peering over my shoulder, 'about keeping in touch. Since my wife died it's been difficult. June. That was her name, I mean. She didn't die in June. She died in January. She was always on the phone, you see, chatting away, morning, noon and night, letting people know what was what, passing on news. But I've never been one for the phone. And especially not now.' He tapped his right ear and I noticed he was wearing a hearing aid. 'I lip-read as much as listen these days, so the phone is a challenge. So I've written to them.' He nodded to the pages of handwriting. 'Now it's just a case of getting it all in there.'

We both looked at the screen.

'Maybe you could read it out, and I could type it?' I suggested. 'Will probably be quicker that way?'

I wanted to give him something to do; I thought it would be less awkward that way. Less pressure than having him sitting there, watching me while I typed.

'Yes, yes. Of course. Good idea. Dear Jerry,' he began, slowly and clearly. 'Billy here . . .' Then as an aside to me he added, 'Jerry's the only one to call me that, of course. That's what they called me in the Navy. I'm just plain William to everyone else.'

245

I nodded and smiled. I hoped William wasn't going to feel the need to explain every sentence of his message to me or we might still be here at Christmas after all.

Luckily, after this, William got into his stride and I helped him let his friend Jerry, along with his daughters Dawn and Abigail and their respective partners and children, know that he had been watching cricket with Peter from down the road, that the doctor was pleased with how his knee was healing and that he had been for lunch at the club – whatever the club was. He asked a lot of questions too – how was the job hunt going (Dawn), how was the new puppy settling in (Abigail) and was there any more news from that lively young lady from the cruise (Jerry).

'How long is it looking?' William said, leaning over my shoulder. I moved my head aside so he could see. 'Hmm,' he said. 'Could do with a little more, I suppose . . . Oh, I know. Tell Dawn I've been to lunch with Audrey. She'll like that. She thinks Audrey is nice to me.'

'Is Audrey not nice to you, then?'

William laughed. 'I have no idea. Haven't seen her for years. Years and years!'

'Oh,' I said, confused. 'So you haven't been for lunch with her?'

William laughed again. 'My dear girl, I haven't done half of these things! But if I tell them I've just been sitting in my living room watching the news or walking along the seafront on my own they'll make a dreadful fuss about me getting "isolated and depressed".'

246

'Oh, right. OK.' This made me feel unspeakably sad but it was hardly my place to be telling William what he could and couldn't say to his own friends and family.

When I'd finished helping William with his correspondence, he bid me farewell, thanking me profusely and promising to practise his typing, as if it made any difference to me.

As I walked home, now very late for dinner, I started to think. Was William exaggerating his social activities to his family any sadder than me pretending I'd been to the Louvre or sharing photos of the aftermath of a party I hadn't even been to? If anything, perhaps I was sadder. After all, William was only trying to put his family's minds at ease.

Why on earth was I doing it?

Results Day

For much of the previous two years, my focus had been very much on one date:

The 24th August. GCSE results day.

I'd read somewhere once about the power of visualisation: imagining our goals turning into reality in glorious, vivid detail.

In the same way other people might have imagined themselves travelling to exotic locations around the world or kissing the boy or girl of their dreams or playing football for England or whatever, my daydreams had been focused squarely on the 24th August.

I'd pull up at school, collect my envelope from reception and rip it open to see a dazzling list of As and A*s, 8s and 9s. Teachers and fellow students would congratulate me and I'd smile shyly and humbly accept their praise. Mum and Dad would cook a special meal for me. I'd pin the results list to the wall above my bed, but sometime later in the day Mum would take it without me knowing, and I'd come downstairs to find she'd framed it, and hung it in pride of place in the downstairs toilet.

However, by the time the day itself rolled around, I could barely be bothered to go into school at all. I didn't even feel like getting out of bed.

Paddy came in, carrying a plate. 'Made you a sandwich, Gracie!' he shouted, resting the plate on my stomach. Two slices of cheese wrapped around a frozen veggie burger. 'Lovely, Paddy. Thanks,' I said, moving the plate off my stomach and sitting up.

Luckily Mum came in as Paddy ran out, with a slightly more appetising plate of toast and a glass of milk.

'How are you feeling?' she asked me, perching on the end of my bed.

I shrugged and took a bite of my toast. I looked out of the window, to avoid engaging with Mum's expression.

'Excited? Bit nervous?'

'Not really,' I said flatly.

Mum looked at me, her head on one side. 'Of course you'll be nervous,' she said. 'That's normal. The last two years have been building up to this day!'

I shook my head hard. I was annoyed but I couldn't quite put my finger on why. Annoyed with her for trying to suggest I felt something I didn't? Annoyed with myself for spending the last two years focused on something I suddenly couldn't care less about?

'I think what your brain's doing, is telling you that you don't care, to stop the nerves getting too much.' She nodded wisely. 'That's what it is.'

'Maybe,' I said. And maybe she was right, but what I thought was more likely, was that I actually didn't care.

Screaming and Hugging

I met Til at the school gates. Already, people from our year were milling around outside the main entrance. Every so often we'd hear a whoop erupt from a little group and we'd see them fall into each other in a hug.

There were a few more downbeat sights too – Toby Harris was sitting on a wall on the phone to someone, his print-out of results hanging down at his side. Lucy Kapoor was crying hard and being comforted by some girl from the year above, but then Lucy Kapoor was always crying so that could've been about anything.

Til was leaning on the railing. 'Ready then?' she said, one eyebrow slightly raised.

I nodded. 'I guess.'

'What's the matter? Ain't today basically Christmas for you?'

I didn't say anything. I could feel myself getting annoyed again, like I had with Mum earlier. I felt like Til was making fun of me, which in itself wasn't unusual or even particularly annoying, but now it was like she was making fun of a person I didn't even think I was any more, so it felt unfair.

'Come on then,' I said, walking off towards reception.

'Let's get it over with.'

'I'm nervous, actually,' Til said as we walked.

'Really?' I was surprised. Til didn't generally admit to any emotions other than bored, annoyed or hungry.

'Yeah, course. I need 4s in maths and English AND a C in science to get on my course.'

'You'll get that though, won't you?'

She shrugged. 'Maths, though . . . Maths is an issue.'

'Well, we'll know in a minute, I suppose.' It seemed too near the moment of truth to bother with any more words of encouragement than that.

And then there we were, brown envelopes in hand.

'Open them then, shall we?' Til said, sighing and looking off into the car park. This was a long way from the excitement of the results day of my daydreams. This was depressing.

I was glad, though, that Til was with me. That I didn't have someone like Lucy crying all over the place, that I wasn't in the middle of one of the groups of girls screaming and hugging. I could not have dealt with that right now.

We opened them. I scanned down the list.

I'd aced them. Three 9s. Five A*s. Three As.

I felt nothing.

I looked over at Til. She was staring at her paper, no emotion on her face.

I didn't know if I should ask, or just say nothing. I folded up my own results sheet and put it into the pocket of my jacket. 'Wanna get a milkshake?' I said, casually.

Til turned her head to look at me. 'I did well, Grace. Like, *really* well.'

Candles

She passed me the paper and I felt my eyes widen. 'Five Bs, two Cs, three 4s and a . . . U?'

'Oh, yeah. Forgot to turn up to German, innit. But who cares about that. I got a B in science, man! An actual B!'

'Wow,' I said. 'That *is* good.'

As we turned out of the school gate, Polly Lynham called over to us. 'Gathering back at mine – you guys coming?'

'Now?' Til said.

Polly nodded as she walked away. 'Yeah. I'm going now. But come whenever.'

'You're not going, are you?' I said, looking at Til out of the corner of my eye. Til did not go to things as a general rule, any more than I did. The only difference was that I tended to turn things down because I wanted to study, whereas Til just couldn't be bothered to talk to people.

'Maybe.' She shrugged. 'Maybe later.'

We ambled down the road away from school and I found myself mumbling my way through an angry and not totally coherent monologue about the pointlessness of it all, about how stupid it was that people were jumping up and down or crying or throwing parties or whatever they were doing, all for some stupid letters on a piece of paper, and how all the information we'd spent all the weeks and months and years cramming into our brains was useless in the real world and why was everyone so brainwashed that they couldn't see it and –

'Jesus Christ, Grace, give it a rest, would you?'

I looked at Til.

'Like, I know you're having your early mid-life crisis or whatever, and I know that whatever ten thousand A*s you're hiding in there don't mean nothing to you but I actually am pretty made up about mine so can you just stop raining all over my candles, yeah?'

I opened my mouth. 'I didn't mean that your –'

Til held up her hand. 'Whatever. It doesn't matter. But either way, you're doing my head in. I'm going round Polly's. You coming?'

I shook my head. I could feel tears in my eyes although I had no idea why. Til was always having a go at me. Why was it bothering me this time?

'See you later then.' Til turned and walked off in the direction of Polly's house.

I walked down the hill in the direction of town and the sea, picking up pace as I went. Rather than feeling guilty for ruining Til's moment, I could feel myself getting more and more worked up.

It *was* all pointless though, wasn't it? All of it. All those facts they'd made us memorise. Yeah, so Til's Bs were good, but what did it mean really, in the end? What is so great about being able to correctly list the sub-atomic particles of an atom? When were we *ever* going to have to do that in real life? What had happened to Til, for goodness' sake? The one person who I thought could be relied on for grumpiness and cynicism, the person who had given me little else for the last two years, during which I had genuinely believed that it all counted for something? Suddenly now, just as I was having a moment of realisation, as I was finally seeing the light, she'd turned on me! She too had been brainwashed.

While I waited for the man to turn green at the crossing at the bottom of Dyke Road, I punched out a few irritable, sarcastic tweets about a few letters on a piece of paper making the last two years of hell worthwhile.

No one replied. Too busy celebrating, I figured.

As I arrived at Vicky and Spider's flat, they were just leaving. Spider was carrying a six-pack of beer.

'Good timing,' he said. 'Beach?'

I nodded but I didn't smile.

'What's up with you, kiddo?' Vicky said, hooking her arm through mine.

'Just got my exam results.'

'Not good?'

'Yeah, good. But . . .' I shrugged. 'I dunno.'

They didn't ask any more questions and I followed them down to the beach, where Spider set about lighting a disposable barbecue.

'You going to show us then?' he said.

'Huh?'

'These exams results.'

I was going to argue but then I didn't see the point. I passed him the paper. He scanned down.

'Woah, Gracie. This is an incredible set of results.'

I shrugged. 'So?'

Vicky took them from him.

'I never know why they make people learn all this stuff,' she said, looking at the page. 'History? What's the point? It's all in the past. French? Who speaks French anyway? Apart from the French, and most of them speak English. Geography? Just buy a map. What's the point in *any* of it?'

'No idea,' I said, picking up a pebble from the ground next to where I was sitting. I passed it from one hand to the other and looked out to sea.

'You know, I dropped out of school when I was fifteen and it hasn't done me any harm,' Vicky said. 'Learnt everything I ever needed from life itself. You know what I mean?'

I nodded without looking at her.

'Anyway, it's behind you now, isn't it?' she said. 'Goodbye to all that . . . rubbish.' On the word 'rubbish' she held the paper over the flickering flames of the barbecue and the whole sheet quickly caught light.

I just blinked. I hadn't had time to stop her even if I wanted to. I hadn't even shown my mum yet. But then . . . Oh, anyway. What did it matter?

I held the smooth, round pebble in my left hand and watched as my results shrivelled down to a flimsy grey film, and then turned to ash.

On the way home, I passed the Age Awareness UK shop just as William was coming out.

'Oh, hello!' he said with a wide smile. 'I have just sent two emails, completely unassisted and it took me less than one hour!'

'Great!' I said.

'And,' he said, 'I opened one reply! From Jerry!'

'Brilliant!'

'Cheerio then, thanks again!' and off he went down the hill.

As I watched him go I had the strange realisation that I felt more proud of helping William keep in touch with his family and friends than I did of any one of those A grades.

PART 6

During which I discover my entrepreneurial spirit and learn to converse with the departed

Money

In the first few days I spent with Vicky and Spider, I didn't give too much thought to where their money came from.

There was always food in the flat – albeit rarely the ingredients of a coherent meal – avocados, satsumas, tubes of Pringles. Raisins in small cardboard packets. And drinks too – I rarely saw either of them without a beer in their hand. On that first day I'd met them in the park, Spider had told me that part of their reason for being in Brighton was to find casual, tourism-based work, but I hadn't seen much evidence of that.

Once, after a heavy afternoon's drinking, Spider played his guitar down on the seafront while Vicky swayed around with her hula hoop in some kind of tribal-looking movement. Spider had put down an old flat-cap to collect money but when they'd eventually been moved on by a Police Community Support Officer ('Not even a real copper!' as Vicky had drunkenly shouted at him), we counted up the coins and found we hadn't even hit the seven-pound mark.

Another day, when I arrived at the flat, Spider told me that Vicky was at work.

'She got a job?'

Spider nodded. 'Yeah, I know. I was surprised too. Sweeping up hair in the barber's on the corner. No idea how long she'll last though. Vicks isn't too keen on being told what to do.'

Spider was right to be concerned. Vicky returned to the flat just two hours into her shift.

She threw her bag down on the sofa.

'What an absolute drongo!' she raged.

'Who?' I asked.

Spider and I exchanged a nervous glance.

'Felipe! The barber. Geriatric moron!' Vicky went to the fridge and took out a beer. 'Kelly rang – you know Kelly, from back home? – and I hadn't spoken to her for like . . . forever, so I had to take the call. So I'm just outside on the phone for like, ten minutes, fifteen max, and he's giving me the eye the whole time. And then he comes out and says, "Are you doing any work today?" Like, seriously sarcastic. I'm not some school kid, for Christ's sake! Absolute drongo,' she said again. 'So I told him to shove it. Told him he could stick the job.'

'But what about the cash, Vicks?' Spider groaned. 'We need that money.'

'Oh, don't you worry about that,' Vicky said. 'Took that from the till before I left.'

She reached into the front pocket of her bag and put two ten-pound notes and a five-pound note on the arm of the sofa. 'No way I was leaving without that.'

Spider looked at the money and sighed. Then he went

into the bedroom and shut the door. It was the nearest thing I had ever seen to an angry outburst from him.

On one occasion, Spider was out with a friend and Vicky asked to borrow a tenner off me to go and buy frozen pizzas from Tesco. I'd stayed in the flat and waited for her to return but, an hour and a half later, I got a text from her telling me to get my 'pasty English butt' down to the beach. I'd done as instructed and no mention was made of the pizzas, and I didn't want to appear uptight by asking about my ten pounds. After all, I reasoned, I had particularly latched on to Vicky and Spider because I admired their carefree, no-stress nature and way of life. I wanted to learn from it. I couldn't start quibbling about the odd tenner – that was hardly the spirit.

Another morning, we went to a cafe for breakfast. It wasn't a fancy place and I think we only had scrambled eggs on toast so I don't think our bill can have come to more than ten pounds. I gave Vicky a small handful of change, she slipped it into the pocket of her dress and wandered off towards the front counter. Fifteen minutes later, we were walking back down Western Road towards the flat and Vicky bought a magazine from a man in a kiosk. I don't know why I noticed it even, but I saw Vicky reach into the same pocket at the front of her dress and take out two of the pound coins I'd given her. I suppose that didn't mean anything in itself – maybe she'd kept my change and paid with a note or whatever – but my instincts must have told me something wasn't quite right because I found myself saying, 'You did pay the bill, at the cafe, didn't you?'

Vicky turned to look at me, frowning. 'I thought you did?'

I shook my head and we both looked at Spider.

'Don't look at me,' he said to Vicky. 'You went off to do it!'

We just looked at each other for another couple of seconds, then Vicky started to giggle.

'Oops. Guess we better not go back there any time soon then.'

Spider laughed too, so in the end that's all I did. I didn't want to be the one to suggest going back like some kind of self-righteous do-gooder.

After that, there were two more non-paying incidents, both of which I was fairly sure were not accidents.

We went for pizzas in an old-fashioned Italian restaurant that let you bring your own drinks. When we'd finished, Vicky said, 'I'll go and ask where the toilet is. While he's not looking, you guys run for it. I'll join you after.'

As before, I wasn't quite sure what to say about this so in the end I just went along with it, even though I felt horribly guilty as we hid behind a skip outside, watching the little old Italian owner sighing and shaking his head as he cleared our table, realising he'd been swindled.

The time after that though, I did say something.

We were in a cafe down on the beach. It was a fish-and-chip place, but it wasn't like all the other places – selling overpriced tiny trays each holding no more than about four chips. This was the real deal – a proper traditional English fish-and-chip restaurant serving huge plates of fresh fish and piles of chips, with thick slices of bread and butter and mushy peas. It seemed to be being run single-handedly by a woman of about sixty with a strong Irish accent. She was lovely to us for the entire duration of our visit – chatting about everything from the weather and the seagulls to her son, and Vicky's childhood in Australia. She'd even thrown in a free basket of bread and bottle of lemonade because she knew 'young folk don't have much money in this day and age'. So when, at the end of the meal, Vicky looked at us, crinkled her nose mischievously and said, 'Ready to run?' I decided to say something.

'I dunno . . .' I said quietly, looking down at the table.

'What's up, kiddo?' Vicky said, her head on one side, looking at me like I was a toddler starting to grizzle for no good reason.

'It's so harsh, just not paying all the time,' I said. I held my breath. I honestly thought this could be the end of our friendship.

Vicky looked at Spider and he looked at her and they smiled at each other in a sort of knowing way, like I was a child asking cute questions about Father Christmas.

'Explain it to her, Spidey,' Vicky said.

Spider leant back in his chair.

'The thing is about the world, Gracie, is that it's all messed up. Wonky, you know? You've seen Vick's paintings, right? Amazing, aren't they?'

I nodded because that seemed to be the expected response.

'Ask her how much money she's made from them.'

I frowned slightly.

'Go on,' Spider prompted, nodding towards Vicky. 'Ask her how much.'

'How much?' I said.

'Nada,' Vicky replied. 'Zilch.'

I looked back at Spider, wondering where this was going.

'Nothing,' Spider said, in case I wasn't clear. 'But then this –' he gestured down at the last few chips on his plate – 'people will pay money for. Stuff that clogs your arteries. Who's making all the money in the world? Bankers. People who sell petrol and cigarettes and pretty teenage boys who write songs about how much they like their own hair. People who are no good. I know she seems like a nice old Irish lady but it's the same, just on a smaller scale. I bet you anything she makes an absolute killing from this place. She's charged us, what?' He picked up the bill from the saucer in the middle of the table. '£17. But I guarantee you it would have cost her no more than three quid to put that food together. Businesses are all about bleeding people dry. We're just trying to redress the balance. Put things right.'

I realised he was right. I had been sucked in because the woman was sweet and friendly and Irish but that didn't change the fact that the world was set up all wrong.

'We can't change the system,' Spider said. 'All we can do is resist from the inside. So yeah, maybe sometimes we don't pay what's asked. But sometimes, we pay what *isn't* asked – when it's what we believe in.'

'Like when?' I said. I was genuinely curious.

'Street musicians. Artists. Charity. All of us has the power to choose where to spend our money. It's the only power we do have, really,' Vicky said.

264

They were both looking at me so intently, so seriously, I don't think it even occurred to me that I'd never seen either of them give any money to any artists or charity collectors, and the only time I'd seen them hand anything over to a street musician was when their friend Andy who played the panpipes down by the pier had asked Vicky for the tenner she owed him.

Everyone's Invited

That evening Twitter and Instagram seemed to be full of photos and updates from an eighteenth birthday party being thrown by some twin boys – Nathan and Blake – from a couple of years above me.

The boys had gone to our school but were now at the college and it seemed like eighty per cent of both institutions had been invited. Needless to say, I did not fall into that eighty per cent, so I was at home, in my bedroom, experiencing the party through the medium of everyone else's increasingly drunk updates and photos.

Nathan and Blake's parents lived in an enormous mansion by Hove Park, complete with swimming pool, tennis courts and a dedicated 'party room' which they seemed to be making quite some use of tonight. I scrolled through the photos feeling a mixture of vague curiosity as to who was there and what they were doing and slight resentment that I had been left out. I saw several familiar faces in various states of drunkenness, including a few people I was on friendly enough terms with, but no one interesting or entertaining enough to make me truly wish I was there instead of at home.

That was until one photo made me stop scrolling immediately, and hold my phone closer to my face for a better look.

It was Sarah, sitting on a bench next to a girl I didn't recognise, laughing at something out of shot. I felt a sharp pang of something I couldn't quite identify – longing, perhaps. Jealousy. I didn't know who the girl was and there was absolutely nothing to suggest that she and Sarah were anything more than friends. In fact, there was nothing to suggest that she and Sarah were anything more than momentary bench companions, but still. Just for a second I felt like I hated her, whoever she was, with her stupid brown curly hair and her laughing mouth. Laughing at a joke that she had heard and that Sarah had heard but that I had not.

I shook my head quickly as if trying to dislodge the uncomfortable feeling and quickly scrolled past the photo and onto a series of photos of Blake with his shirt off, being painted by a group of three girls with some kind of neon paint.

But then I was forced to pause again, because here was another familiar face.

Til.

Til! Since when did Til know Nathan and Blake? And since when did Til go to parties? And, more to the point, since when did Til go to parties without telling me about them?

Since now apparently. Here she was. Here Til was, at a party, with Sarah – my Sarah – probably having a tremendously good time and agreeing what a dreadful, Australian-snogging, yellow-legged bore I was.

I closed my phone and shoved it under my pillow crossly. I lay on my back in bed looking at the ceiling and tried to tell myself that I had a much better time with Vicky and Spider than I ever would at some stupid house party full of morons from school.

I couldn't shake the irritation though. The jealousy. Why was it that, no matter how much fun you were having, everyone else was always having more fun?

And why was it that they were always having the fun together?

Without you?

Nagging

My bedroom, by this stage of the summer, was an absolute disgrace.

One morning Ollie came in to ask to borrow my phone charger and as he hovered in the doorway while I unplugged it, he said, 'You're really letting things go, eh, Gracie?'

'What do you mean?' I demanded, before looking around me and realising exactly what he meant.

There were plates of half-eaten sandwiches – both real ones and Paddy's more questionable offerings – dotted around the carpet. I'd stopped using my wardrobe at all and clothes were draped over my chair and in piles in the middle of the floor. My desk, once the epitome of organisation, was hidden under a carpet of crisp packets and bus tickets and –

'Ugh, gross,' Ollie said, looking at it. 'You keep your dirty pants in the middle of your desk now?'

I rolled my eyes.

'It's not that bad,' I said. 'I can clean it up in no time. Look.'

I took my bin over to the edge of my desk and in one smooth arm movement, swept every item straight into it. Dirty pants and everything.

'You can't just throw your pants away. What you going to do when you run out?'

I shrugged. 'Wear yours again.'

Ollie just shook his head and took my charger from me.

'Oh, guess what?' he said.

'What?' I said grumpily.

'I'm going to college.'

'What do you mean? When?'

'In September. I'm going to do a BTEC in Music Production.'

I laughed, and not in a kind way. 'Why?'

'What do you mean why?'

'Like, what's the point? You're not going to be a pop star.'

Ollie looked at me, his head on one side. He looked bemused, almost, like he was finding me puzzling in some way. 'I never said I was. I don't know where it's going to take me. But I reckon I'll enjoy the course and that's a start.'

'If you say so.' I was lying on my bed not looking at him, scrolling through my phone.

Paddy was downstairs in the kitchen. 'Gracie!' he called. 'I made you a sandwich!'

'I'm not hungry, thanks,' I mumbled.

Then Mum's voice came from somewhere else in the house. 'Oh, just humour him, Grace. He'll kick off again otherwise.'

I trudged downstairs to receive this latest creation. I was surprised to see that for the first time in his life, Paddy had grasped the concept of a sandwich made out of two pieces of bread.

'Padster!' I ruffled his hair. 'You made an actual sandwich!'

He beamed proudly.

'What's in it?'

'Surprise,' he said.

Luckily I decided to investigate the exact nature of this surprise before taking a bite. When I peeled back the top slice of bread I found a thick wodge of toilet roll soaked in something that may have been orange juice, or may have been something more upsetting.

'Lovely,' I smiled at Paddy. 'What a treat.'

Dad was sitting at the kitchen table, cradling a cup of tea in his hands and looking out the window. He looked sad. Wistful. I had been meaning to say something, and now seemed like the time.

'Mum said you were sad about Nan,' I said awkwardly. I managed to make it sound more like an accusation than empathy. 'So . . . sorry about that. I'm sad too.' I cringed. I sounded like a children's picture book. *My First Emotions. I'm sad. Are you sad?*

Dad turned to look at me. He sighed. 'Yeah. It's not just that though. Not just missing her. I suppose it's just made me realise – remember – how life is short. We don't get a lot of it, do we? And between you and me, Grace, sometimes I'm not totally sure how well I'm using mine.'

I was alarmed.

Dad was cheery. Dad danced the Macarena in the queue at Asda and made the same joke about me having missed Christmas every time I got up after 9 a.m. Dad did not get morose and despair that he was wasting his life. I didn't know what to say.

271

Luckily, Dad seemed to abruptly snap out of his gloom so I didn't have to say anything.

He went over to the dishwasher and started unloading it. 'Are you out today?'

I nodded. 'Probably.'

'You're never in, these days, it seems!' he said brightly.

I shrugged. 'It's summer.'

Dad nodded. 'I know, I know. But you can bring people back here too, you know! What about Til? Haven't seen her for a while.'

'She's busy. Getting ready for college.'

'Is there anything you need to be doing? To get ready for the new term? Not long now . . .'

'Oh for god's sake!' I exploded. 'No, I don't need to be doing anything. I don't need to be tidying my room or reading school books or working in some pointless summer job. Why can't you all leave me alone? You've literally just said about wasting life! Just now! So stop trying to make me waste mine!'

Dad just stood there, looking at me, a teatowel in his hand.

I marched down the hallway and out of the front door, slamming it behind me.

The Spirit Whisperer

It was, I think, in the fourth week that I'd known Vicky and Spider that we were watching telly in their lounge when a programme called *Spirit Whisperer* came on.

The Spirit Whisperer was a man called Dale Keller and the concept of the programme was that he'd invite members of the audience to come up to the stage, bringing with them a photo of a dearly departed loved one. Dale would then sit opposite the person at a small square table so they could watch while he attempted to make contact with the dead person's spirit.

In the episode we saw, Dale's guest (victim?) was a woman called Nancy and she came to the stage armed with a photo of a man she told us was her brother, Mark, who had died in a mountaineering accident four years ago.

'I just want to know he's warm enough,' Nancy tearfully told Dale. 'It's on my mind all the time. The terrible idea of him being cold and wet still, wherever he is.'

Dale nodded seriously and took the photo from Nancy and placed it between his palms. He closed his eyes and began to breathe deeply. Nancy, along with the rest of the audience, waited anxiously.

'I'm getting a strong sense of a beard,' Dale said, moving his hand around his own chin, his eyes still closed. 'A brown . . . or maybe even reddish . . . beard.'

Nancy's eyes widened. 'Oh yes,' she said, breathlessly. 'He did have a beard. He shaved it off a few years before the accident. It was a big beard though, for some years.'

Dale nodded slowly, as if this confirmed the messages he was receiving.

'And a hat,' Dale said. 'I'm sensing a hat. Woollen.'

'Yes,' Nancy said again. 'He did wear a woolly hat sometimes.'

'Oh, please!' Vicky said, throwing a grape at the screen in disgust. 'So the dude once had a beard and owned a woolly hat. I could have told you that much.'

Spider sniggered and I had to agree it was all absolute nonsense.

Dale went on, listing all the elements of Nancy's brother Mark that he was 'sensing' – the fact he liked dogs, that he'd once been to Scotland, that he didn't like Christmas. Nancy lapped it all up.

Even when Dale got it completely wrong he managed to work the situation to his favour. 'He liked a drink . . . whisky?' he'd suggested.

But Nancy pointed out that in fact, Mark had never drunk a drop his whole life. 'Our father was an alcoholic, you see. We both swore we would never go that way.'

Dale just nodded wisely as if this all made perfect sense. 'Yes,' he said. 'That's it. I'm getting a strong alcohol message

274

from him. That's what it is. A dislike of it. I can smell it almost, now.' He theatrically sniffed the air in front of him.

Once Dale had impressed Nancy with enough of his insights into what kind of a man Mark had been, he was able to move onto the probably entirely fictional business of giving Nancy messages.

'He says that yes, he is warm enough. He says not to worry. He says to look after the girls.'

Nancy frowned.

'Kids maybe? Your daughters? Or Mark's?' Dale said tentatively.

Nancy shook her head. 'Mark didn't have children. And I have just one son . . . Oh!' she said suddenly. 'He's talking about his rose bushes! The wally. He always called them 'she'. Tell him they're still going strong, in my garden now. They're doing well.'

Dale smiled indulgently at Nancy. 'You just told him yourself.'

Nancy beamed.

By the time it was time for Nancy to depart the stage and the next bereaved relative to step up, Spider had had enough. 'I cannot watch another second of this.'

'Total morons,' Vicky agreed. 'All of them.'

'No way,' I said, laughing. 'Look at this.'

I passed my phone over to Spider to show him Dale's Wikipedia page. 'He's absolutely loaded. From doing that!'

'Dale owns a two-million-pound mansion in the Cotswolds as well as properties in Los Angeles, Stockholm and Cape Town. His net worth is estimated to be eighteen point four million pounds,' Spider read.

'Eighteen point four mill!' Vicky said, shaking her head. 'From doing that! Jesus, Mary and Joseph in heaven. What is this world?'

'*We* should become psychics,' Spider muttered, grabbing the remote and flicking through the channels. 'Clearly money in it.'

'We should, you know,' Vicky said suddenly.

We looked at her.

'What?' Spider said.

'Become psychics. Seriously. We need money and that is apparently where the money is.'

'I don't think you can order psychic powers off the internet like one of those dodgy print-out degrees,' Spider said.

'We don't need psychic powers,' Vicky said, sitting up now. 'Psychic powers aren't even a real thing, you moron! Dale whatever-his-name-is hasn't got psychic powers any more than any of us have, and look at him – raking it in.'

I thought about this. She had a point. But if it really was that easy – if anyone could just set themselves up as psychic and demand money for spouting some made-up details about a few random coincidences, then why wasn't everyone doing it?

I put this question to Vicky.

'Balls. *Cojones*. You've just got to have the guts to stand up there and do it. That's all it is.'

'Maybe,' Spider said uncertainly, as he started to flick through the channels again.

Just then, the TV cut out and so did the lights.

'Oh Christ,' Vicky sighed.

I looked at Spider.

'Meter's empty,' he said, standing up and looking at a box on the wall.

'Go top it up then,' Vicky said, irritably. She was now lying on the sofa with her legs hanging over the arm scrolling through her phone.

'What with, Vicks?' Spider said. 'We haven't got money to keep pumping into it.'

Then he went into the kitchen and came back with three candles and a box of matches. He positioned them in a row along the coffee table in the lounge and lit them.

'We'll just do without power for tonight. We don't need it anyway. We were only watching junk. We can sit. And talk.'

'Sounds fascinating,' Vicky said, still without looking up.

Sensing the tension in the room and as it was getting late anyway, I made my excuses and headed home.

Madame Violet Verano

The next time I called in at the flat was the following afternoon.

'Gracie,' Vicky said, beaming widely as she opened the front door. 'Come and take a look at this. I'm a god's honest genius.'

She led me by the hand into the lounge where she handed me a wodge of A4 papers. They were all copies of the same thing – a poster, hand drawn, but very professionally so.

Madame Violet Verano
Psychic medium and clairvoyant
Get in touch with the dearly departed

There was a number at the bottom.

'Your mobile number?'

Vicky nodded proudly.

'You're Madame Violet Verano?'

She pulled the hood of her cardigan up so it cloaked her face and pushed her fingertips together and held them about chest height.

'Yes, child,' she purred in an accent that was somewhere between Jamaican and Welsh. 'I am Madame Violet Verano. My ears are attuned to the voices of the dead. How can I help yooooou?'

Then she burst into hysterical cackling and pulled her hood back down.

I looked at her with one eyebrow raised and smiled. 'This is never going to work. You are surely not really going to try it?'

Spider came in to join us. 'You'll be surprised the things Vicks goes ahead with once she's made her mind up.'

Vicky took my hand. 'Come, come, ye of little faith,' she said, once again adopting the peculiar accent. 'Come into my chamber.'

'Chamber?' I said as I followed Vicky to the bedroom. 'Is that really what you're going to call it? Isn't that where people go to be executed?'

'Hmm,' Vicky said, frowning. 'Maybe you're right. What should I call it? My studio? My boudoir?'

When Vicky opened the bedroom door I had to admit that, whatever she decided to call it, she'd done an impressive job with the space.

She'd covered the bed with a red-and-gold woven blanket, and in the middle of it she'd positioned a small circular table. She climbed on to the bed and sat with her legs crossed, her palms resting on the table.

'This is me in position,' she explained. 'I'll sit here, and they can sit opposite me. The customers, I mean. Not the ghosts. The ghosts will probably just . . . float around.' She waved her hands around in the space either side of her head.

She'd draped a sheet of sheer red fabric over the window, which served the dual purpose of blocking out the view of the tattoo parlour opposite and bathing the room in a warm, dim glow. She'd cleared away all the bottles of moisturiser and deodorant and all the books and DVDs from the shelves on the wall and had lined them instead with a row of flickering candles. There was a speaker somewhere – I couldn't see where – emitting some strange panpipe music.

'Wow,' I said.

'I know, right?' Vicky said, grinning. 'And wait till I'm in my costume.'

'You have a costume?'

'Of course!' Vicky said, jumping off the bed and going over to the wardrobe. 'That's the best bit. Get out. I'm going to put it on now. I want to give you the full effect.'

I did as I was told and a few minutes later Vicky emerged from the bedroom wearing a long purple robe – a sort of cross between a dressing gown and a wizard's dress. Her hair was piled up on top of her head with a few loose tendrils falling over her face. She had on some long dangly earrings – one like a raindrop, the other a star – and thick gold bangles rattled around her wrists. Her make-up was the most surprising element though. Heavy black eyeliner, thick mascara and bright red lips, and she'd coloured her eyebrows in completely so where they'd once been blonde and barely noticeable, they were now black and thick and – for some reason – joined in the middle. I don't suppose I'd really stopped to think about it before, but it occurred to me then that I'd never seen Vicky in make-up before. She looked like a different person. She looked mysterious. I was impressed.

'Why have you done that to your eyebrows?' I asked, peering at her.

'Oh,' she said, turning to the mirror to examine them. 'I always think striking eyebrows are a good way to make an impression. Might have overdone it though, I admit.'

'You are mad,' I told her.

'Aw, babe!' She crinkled her nose and ruffled my hair. 'You say the sweetest things.'

Down to Business

'So how's it going to work then?' I said, sitting down on the sofa.

'You want to know the business plan?'

'There's a business plan?'

'Of course, honey!'

It did cross my mind that only a few days ago Spider had lectured me on the evils of private enterprise. But this didn't seem anything to do with that. This was different.

'It's pretty simple,' Vicky said. 'First thing is that we advertise, obviously. Get the word out. Let people know that there's a hot new psychic in town with a direct line to the other side. Then people call up, make appointments. We don't let them have one straight away – we make it clear that Madame Violet is very much in demand – so by the time they get in the door, they're already half convinced of her – of my! – powers.'

'And people have to pay?'

'Well, duh! A specialist service like this one doesn't come cheap. A fifteen-minute session is fifty pounds.'

'Fifty pounds!' I said. 'There's no way anyone will pay that.'

'Course they will!' Vicky said, grinning. 'Thing is, Gracie baby, this is important stuff, you know? People are going to be getting messages from their actual real-life dead relatives. We're talking literally life and death. People say, "Oh I'd give my right arm to have just one more conversation with him," don't they? So fifty pounds is nothing. And if I said, "Oh that'll be two-pound-fifty please," people would be suspicious, wouldn't they? This isn't some dodgy end-of-the-pier set-up to give tourists a cheap thrill on a Saturday afternoon. This is the real deal!'

I think Vicky had actually managed to talk herself into it. To convince even herself that she genuinely had the power to help people make contact with the dead. And maybe that wasn't a bad thing. They always say you've got to believe in yourself if you expect anyone else to, don't they?

The three of us set out to put up the posters across town. We were in high spirits, all of us. I was relieved after the tension that the money worries had caused in the flat the day before. I'd started to wonder if I was part of the problem. I often picked up supplies on my way over, but maybe I wasn't paying my fair share. Maybe they thought I was a freeloader.

As I had walked home after watching Vicky and Spider stress and snap at each other over the electricity meter I'd started to wonder if maybe I'd been too quick to see Vicky and Spider's life as some kind of perfect bohemian dream. When it came down to it, was it going to turn out that they didn't have any more fun or freedom than anyone else? But now, as we swaggered around town, Spider with a beer can in his hand, Vicky spontaneously breaking into song in Madame Violet's strange Welsh-Jamaican accent, all three of us laughing and laughing and laughing, things felt good again.

This was definitely fun. This was definitely living. Just thinking of something silly and crazy and hilarious and just going out and doing it.

On the way home that day, I decided to go and see Til. I knew I'd been neglecting her but every time we'd met up recently things had been tense. It just seemed to me that the nearer we got to September, the more she was thinking – and talking – about the new term and the less I wanted to hear it.

'Oh, it's you,' she said, when her mum let me in and I went into her bedroom.

'Yes,' I said pointlessly. 'Me.'

She didn't say anything else. She was sitting on her bed looking at her laptop. She didn't look up at me. I felt like I was in trouble.

I sat down on the end of the bed. 'What you doing?'

'Reading about psychology.'

'Why?'

'Why not?

Silence. Til still didn't look up.

'I –' I began, but at exactly the same time Til started to speak too, so I stopped. 'Sorry,' I said. 'What were you going to say?'

'Nothing,' she mumbled.

I sighed. 'What is your problem? Why are you being so miserable all the time?'

She looked at me then. 'Because my mum got the sack, OK? She doesn't have a job and she's just in bed and I don't know what we're going to do.'

'Oh,' I said. 'Why?'

Til shrugged. 'Who knows? Because she never turns up? Because she cries all the time all over the customers? How should I know?'

'Well, it will be OK,' I said. 'I'm sure she'll get another job. I'm sure it will be OK.'

'Great,' Til said, turning back to her screen. 'That's all fine then. As long as you're sure it's going to be OK, I'm sure it will. You can get back to your new mates now. I'll be fine here. Just fine.'

I just looked at her. What did she want me to say? It wasn't my fault her mum was such an enormous sad-sack. I was just trying to say something kind to make her feel better.

What did she want me to say?

I stood up. 'I'll go then.'

She didn't reply, or even look up.

Restructuring

At home that evening, Dad was sitting in the living room.

The curtains were drawn and the room was bathed in a gloomy blue light. It was too hot in there and he was watching the cricket with the sound turned down.

'What's the matter?' I said.

'Nothing.' He didn't even look up from the screen. He was slouched in his chair, the remote control resting on one knee.

Mum came in and replaced the flowers on the table with some new ones. 'What's the matter with Dad?' I said, as if he wasn't right there.

'Bad news at work,' she said gently. 'Restructuring.'

She touched his shoulder gently and left the room.

Dad sighed.

'Are you going to lose your job?' I asked him.

He shook his head and shrugged. 'Who knows. Didn't think I even liked the job until I thought they were going to take it away from me.'

He flicked the telly off and left the room.

I found Mum in her bedroom, changing the pillowcases on the bed.

'Is Dad really going to lose his job?' I asked.

'I shouldn't think so,' she said.

'So why's he so grumpy?'

She thought for a moment, shaking the pillowcase by the corners to get the pillow to sit neatly inside. 'I think it's because he only took that computer job to be sensible. It was hardly his calling. He wanted to be outdoors, didn't he. To teach sailing or orienteering or something. But he was careful and took a sensible job with sensible hours and sensible money because he wanted security for himself, and for all of us. But now he feels like there hasn't been any reward for being so sensible.'

I nodded. That did sound annoying, to be fair.

'Is the sex clinic your calling?' I asked Mum suddenly.

She laughed. 'When you've got three children and a clinic full of itchy crotches to look after, you don't have much time to think about callings.' Then she added, 'I don't think I believe in callings, really. At least not for me.'

'No?'

She shook her head slowly. 'When I was young, the thing back then was to tell you that there was one person out there for everyone. Magazines, your mates – they were all obsessed with the idea. One true love. One soul mate. But then I got older and realised that probably wasn't true. There are plenty of people for everyone. Plenty of people perfectly able to love each other and share a life together.

'These days everyone wants to believe that they have one true calling, that one thing they're just born to do and if they can only find it they'll never have to do anything they don't like again.

'But we all like lots of things. And we all don't like lots of things. And the reality is, we'll probably have a bit of both in our lives. So no, the sex clinic isn't my calling. But I like it just fine. I like my life just fine. God knows, it's a lot better than what some people end up with.'

Black and White

A few days later, one of Mum's friends came to the house and she and Mum were sitting at the kitchen table eating carrot cake and drinking coffee. I was in my bedroom.

'Grace!' Mum called. 'Come down here a minute.'

I reluctantly did as I was told.

'Grace, love, tell Julia what you got in your exams.'

I made a face. 'Three 9s, five A*s and three As,' I mumbled.

'Wow,' Julia said. 'Very impressive.'

'Isn't it just?' Mum said, smiling. 'You know, Gracie, I don't think Dad and I have even seen them written down, in black and white. Will you show me?'

'Why?' I demanded crossly. 'You think I'm lying?'

Mum blinked, and looked at me, her head on one side, bemused. 'Of course not. I'd just like to see it.'

I sighed. 'I'll show you later.' I left the kitchen before she could press the point.

Paying Customers

When I got to Vicky and Spider's later that day, Vicky proudly announced that she had not one but two clients booked in for their first session with Madame Violet.

'OK, so two is only two, but it's a start, hey? This kind of thing has to spread through word of mouth, you know?'

I nodded enthusiastically. 'Absolutely. Two is amazing, I'm impressed.' And I was. 'And they both know the price? I mean, they're both going to spend fifty pounds on this . . . on you?'

Vicky laughed. 'Yes, kiddo, they are! I told you to have faith.'

Something I hadn't realised during the early planning stages of our new business was the role that Vicky and Spider had in mind for me. Apparently it was important that I was present for all the appointments, to welcome people, to see them into the flat, and to deal with the money side of things. I was basically to act as a kind of executive PA to the great Madame Violet.

'I need to maintain an aura of mystique,' Vicky explained. 'It's damaging to the image if I'm struggling with the sticky door catch or scrabbling around looking for change in my purse. You need to do all that for me, so I can stay in character in the room.'

'Right,' I said. 'Fine.' I thought it sounded simple enough. 'So what's Spider going to do then?'

'Oh god,' Vicky laughed. 'Spider has to stay behind the scenes. A beardy bloke with tattoos is not going to give people confidence. He'll be out.'

Our first customer arrived at four o' clock that afternoon. She was a woman called Lilian. She wore a thick fleece and walking boots as if she was coming to us straight from a hiking expedition and she brought with her a long pearl necklace that, completely without prompting, she informed me used to belong to her grandmother.

'Have I got the right place?' Lilian asked, looking around her nervously as we trudged up the stairs to the second-floor flat. 'Isn't quite what I imagined?'

'Oh yes, absolutely,' I said confidently. 'People never expect it to look like this but that's because of all the media brainwashing out there these days. People think of psychics and fortune tellers as people who live in gypsy caravans or in little huts in the woods but that's all nonsense. Fairy-tale stuff. This is where Madame Violet lives so this is where she carries out her work. She needs to be completely relaxed in her environment for her powers and senses to be at full capacity.'

I was saying all this entirely off the top of my head but I was rather pleased with the explanation. And hiking Lilian certainly seemed to buy it well enough.

I opened the door to the bedroom to show Lilian in, and

Vicky lifted her arms, letting her sleeves billow, and said, 'Welcome, welcome, Lilian, my dear. Oh, you are *exactly* as I imagined. I knew it was you at once.'

I made sure not to catch Vicky's eye or to allow myself even the smallest smirk at this opening line. I bowed my head in a manoeuvre that I intended to represent my deference to the great Madame Violet, and I then excused myself. I was glad my role didn't require me to be present during any more of Vicky's performance as I was quite sure I would have felt the need to giggle throughout.

The door opened fifteen minutes later and Vicky stood in the doorway and kissed Lilian extravagantly on both cheeks. Lilian didn't say much as I showed her down the stairs and out of the flat. She seemed slightly shell-shocked.

'How was it?' I asked Vicky as soon as I got back up to the flat. 'Did you get away with it?'

Vicky laughed, making her ornate earrings rattle, and took a can of Coke out of the fridge. 'I more than got away with it, doll! I had her eating out of the palm of my hand.'

'But how?' I said with a bemused smile. 'How on earth did you manage to convince her you were really talking to . . . who was it? Her mum?'

'Grandma,' Vicky said, going over to the mirror and retying her headscarf. 'Easy, mate. Eeeeeasy. She gave it to me on a plate. "I'm seeing a dress," I said. "A beautiful dress . . ." Her eyes light up and she says, "Oh yes, she used to be a ballroom dancer. She had so many beautiful dancing dresses when she was younger." And then bingo-bango, I'm away.

I'm "seeing" trophies and crowds and sparkly dancing shoes. And anything I said, the woman would feed me a little more info. I just had to jump on the details and run with it.'

'Did you have to do the voice?' I asked. 'A grandma voice?'

Vicky laughed. 'No, babe! I wasn't pretending to be possessed! I just passed on some nice messages. "I'm watching you from up here, little Lilian. I like to see you happy." All that rubbish. Just told her what she wanted to hear, and off she trots, pleased as pineapple. And I'm pretty pleased myself because . . .' Vicky put her hand down the front of her robe and pulled out two twenty-pound notes and one ten. 'Fifty smackers! How easy was that?'

I shook my head and smiled. 'Mad.'

'Hey, you know what, kiddo, if it turns out I'm a natural at this, I can put you in touch with your old nan if you like.' She put on her Welsh-Jamaican accent. 'Nan, oh Nan, are you there? Gracie's missing you!'

She burst into one of her customary cackles and I managed a weak chuckle, although I didn't feel really like laughing at all. What struck me about what she'd just said is the brief wave of hope that had washed over me. For one tiny moment, I think the irrational part of my brain actually hoped Nan was there – that somehow she could make contact through Vicky. And that made me think, if I could have that thought, however fleetingly, when I knew full well that Vicky had no powers whatsoever, then how powerful was this stuff to the people we were trying to convince?

Wanting to believe something that badly, had a damaging effect on your rational judgement, that was for sure.

Going Concern

Over the next few days I welcomed another five or six clients to the flat, and showed them to Madame Violet's studio. They were definitely all of a certain type, I noticed. Nervous, a bit shy. Maybe even a little bit unhinged.

Vicky had been lucky so far, with the people we'd had interested in taking up our dubious service. They were all so keen to be told what they wanted to hear that they invariably revealed crucial clues almost at once, making Vicky's job no more complicated than delivering some meaningless platitudes in her bizarre accent and closing her eyes at the right moment, as if disappearing off to some higher level of consciousness.

One evening when we'd just said goodbye to our third customer of the week, Spider raised a point that I too had been worried about: 'I'm starting to feel a bit guilty, you know? Cashing in on these people's grief. Are we taking advantage?'

I looked at Vicky, keen to hear her answer to this. She, of course, had one.

'Look at it this way, babe: these guys are sad and lonely

and missing whoever they're missing. They come in here, I tell them what they want to hear – that the dead dudes are happy and looking after them and that they'll see them again one day. This stuff makes them happy! Fifty pounds is a small price to pay for happiness, isn't it? Who *cares* if it's not true? Since when did the truth make anyone happy? The truth is probably that the dead rellies are nowhere at all. Dead and cold in the ground. How is telling them that any better? My conscience is clear. I'm providing a service here. A happiness service. There's nothing wrong with charging for a service.'

She made a compelling case, I thought. If our customers left us with thoughts of their relatives safe and happy and out there, somewhere, waiting for them, how could that really be a bad thing? Maybe honesty wasn't the best policy, not always.

And there was another, less honourable, reason that made me want to keep going with the scheme:

The cash.

The money was so good! Madame Violet's studio had only been trading for a week and already we'd made six hundred pounds.

We sat on the floor of the lounge and I counted out the notes I'd been collecting in the inside pocket of my jacket into piles. I wasn't yet sure what share of the money might be mine, and I didn't like to ask, scared they might tell me this was their flat, so their money, or that I'd already taken enough from them by hanging around and eating their food for weeks on end.

'I can't believe it's so easy,' Spider said, shaking his head. 'It's mad.'

I felt the same. I'd grown up being taught the value of hard work, believing that the only way to get anywhere in life was to get your head down and put in the hard graft, no matter how boring or difficult it got. Since the day of my hospital visit, I'd been questioning the way I'd spent the last few years, but now more than ever I couldn't believe I'd been so naive.

Why in god's name had I spent my whole life memorising facts about oil refineries and scribbling equations in an exercise book and reading poems written by some old guy two hundred years ago when it was this easy to make money?

Not Going Back

With the earnings from our first few clients, Vicky and Spider took care of a few basics – topping up the electricity meter, restocking the kitchen with chocolate and cheese and beers, replacing the dead lightbulb in the bathroom – but then we started to dream big.

'We could make enough to really do something,' Spider said. 'All those real adventures on our list. The Taj Mahal. Great Wall of China. Or we could travel around Europe or something,' Spider said. 'We could get an Interrail ticket. See Berlin. Bucharest. Krakow.'

Vicky rolled her eyes. 'Or we could go somewhere that isn't a total dive. Like Paris or Rome?'

Spider sighed and smiled. 'Whatever. We could do it all. It's been a long time since we've been able to afford to travel anywhere,' he told me. 'I've got itchy feet. It's a shame you can't come, Gracie.'

'Why can't she come?' Vicky demanded.

'She's got school soon, hasn't she,' Spider said.

'Oh,' Vicky said, picking at her nails, looking bored by the very mention of the subject. 'Yeah. That.'

'Yeah,' I repeated flatly. 'That.'

I got up and went over to the window. I stuck my head out and looked down at the street. There was an old woman walking a tiny Yorkshire terrier, pulling on his lead to try to stop him drinking water from the gutter. There were two men in their twenties snaking in and out of parked cars on skateboards. A woman came out of one of the flats opposite and dumped a big black rubbish bag in the communal bin. I didn't know any of these people or anything about their lives but I felt all of them were freer than me. None of them would have to go back to school in a few weeks to spend hour after hour in an airless classroom trying to cram meaningless information into their brains.

'Maybe I won't go back,' I said suddenly. 'Maybe I'm done with all that.'

Spider chuckled gently and Vicky just nodded and said, 'Uh huh,' as she flicked through the TV channels.

They weren't taking me seriously, and I don't think I'd even said it seriously, but just for a moment, I let myself run with the thought. What if I didn't go back to school? What if I really was done with that, with all of it?

I didn't really trust this idea though. I still felt that maybe the whole summer had been a bubble, that I was having some kind of psychological reaction to the stress of my exams and that when I'd finished blowing off steam, I'd snap out of it. Or that Til was right and I was having an early mid-life crisis. I wasn't sure it was going to last. I was still hoping that something miraculous would happen in the next few weeks and somehow the idea of going back to school would seem bearable.

It was only because of Dad's inheritance money that I ended up saying anything at all.

It was just before dinner that evening. Dad was peeling potatoes and I went into the kitchen to get a drink.

'I heard from the solicitor today,' Dad said

'What solicitor?'

'The one dealing with your nan's estate.'

'Oh, OK.' I paused and sat down at the kitchen table.

'She left me some money,' Dad said. 'Well, all of us really. For the family.'

'How much?' seemed like the obvious question but I didn't want to appear cold, so I just said, 'Right. OK.'

'Nearly twenty grand,' Dad said anyway.

'Twenty *thousand* pounds?'

Dad nodded and turned to look at me, grabbing a tea towel from the radiator and drying his hands on it. 'Yeah, could make quite a difference.'

I nodded.

Twenty thousand pounds.

Already in my head I had images of a safari or a Caribbean cruise or even something wild, like trekking in Peru. Maybe Mum and Dad would just jack in their jobs and we'd head off, like one of those gap-year families. This would be the perfect excuse not to go back to school.

'So, what . . . what are you going to do with it?'

'Well . . .' Dad came and joined me at the table. 'Mum and I were talking and we wondered if we should keep some of it to help with your university costs, but to be honest, we've been saving for that since you were born so we're probably covered. So then we were thinking, you're going to be really up against it work-wise next year and the year after, and maybe for the few years after that – university, of course, but then maybe you'll want to do a Masters too – so we thought we could extend into the loft, move Paddy's room up there, then you could have his little room as a study? Somewhere to keep all your books and notes, a decent desk. Maybe a whiteboard on one wall for lists and timetables and whatever. A proper little base. What do you think?'

Dad was grinning at me like he was painting an image of paradise and offering it to me on a plate. And to be fair, there was a time when that's exactly how I would have seen it.

Not now though.

Now, all I was hearing was that:

My parents – like everyone else, probably – had written off the next five, seven, *ten* years of my life to study and revision.

People thought that my idea of the perfect treat was to be given a tiny box room lined with textbooks to while away hour after pointless hour.

The reasonable, calm side of my brain knew that Mum and Dad had conjured up this proposal to be thoughtful and helpful and because they thought it was something I'd genuinely like, but the unreasonable, frustrated, furious side of me cancelled all that out.

All that side of me had to say about this plan was:

'I can think of literally no worse way to spend that money.'

'Oh,' Dad said, taken aback. 'OK.'

At that point, Mum came in.

'Not a lot of enthusiasm for the study plan,' Dad told her quietly.

'No?' Mum said, frowning, joining us at the table.

'I don't want a stupid study!' I shouted. At the same time I swiped over a bar stool, sending it crashing to the floor. My voice was going – cracking – like I was going to cry. I never lost it like that. Never. I had no idea what had happened to me.

They both just looked at me, blinking.

Then Mum frowned. 'I don't know what's happened to you these last few weeks, Grace, but you've not been very nice.'

'Well, I'm sorry,' I said, standing up so hard my chair fell over. 'I'm sorry if it would be easier for you if I spent the next ten years sitting at my desk being good and quiet at writing pointless essays and getting pointless grades in pointless exams. But maybe I actually want to do some stuff!'

I could see Mum getting ready to lose her temper with me, but Dad put his hand on her arm.

'It's OK to be a bit worried about A levels, love,' he said calmly. 'It will be a big change, but you'll get into the swing of it, just like you always do.'

'Maybe I don't want to get into the swing of it,' I said, quieter now. I didn't feel so angry suddenly, just miserable.

'No pain, no gain,' Mum said.

'But what gain?' I protested. 'All I gain by doing exams is the chance to do more exams that are really boring and then get a job that is really boring and be bored and fed up for the whole rest of my life!'

At this point, Ollie skulked into the kitchen and flicked the kettle on.

'So you've just worked out that life's all boring then?' he said with a yawn.

Dad shot him a sharp look.

'Not helpful, Oliver,' Mum said.

'He's right, though,' I said, leaning back against the wall and rubbing my eyes. 'It is.'

'It's not,' Mum said. 'It's just hard work. But you get out what you put in.'

'But that's not even true! That's just what they tell you to make you keep working, like one day it will pay off. But when? When will it? When you're retired and practically dead? If I work hard all my life I can have a high-class coffin lined with gold silk? Fantastic. Brilliant. Great.'

Dad sighed. 'But that's the way the game works, Gracie. You work hard, you get paid, you live. No one's going to pay you to run around with your new hippy friends. Who, by the way, are clearly responsible for this sudden change in attitude.'

'They're not hippies. What does that even mean? They just know how to live. *And* they know how to make money.'

'By busking?' Ollie said, with his eyebrow raised.

'No, not busking,' I said, sighing.

And then I sat back down at the table and told them about Madame Violet Verano, and how we were offering people hope and comfort and in return we were making some good money.

When I'd finished, Ollie chuckled and shook his head. 'Fraud,' he said. 'Excellent.'

'It certainly isn't excellent,' Mum said sharply. 'But it is fraud, Grace. What do you think you're playing at?'

I looked around at them all, Mum and Dad looking at me, mild frowns on their faces. Ollie slouching there in the same filthy pyjama bottoms he always wore. I felt like they were crushing me, trying to squash me into a box, to make me be like them. To make me be the unremarkable, predictable good girl I'd always been, to make life nice and easy for them.

Why were they trying to make me be like them? With their jobs in offices pushing bits of paper around? I didn't even know what they did all day so I was pretty sure it couldn't be changing the world.

What was the point of it all? Doing what you're supposed to doesn't get you anywhere. It just got you out of the way so the people with the smart ideas and the motivation and the bravery could get on and have some fun. I didn't want to be one of the pushed-out-of-the-way ones. I wanted to have the ideas. I wanted to make money and travel around Europe on the train and do all the other stuff on our list.

I rattled through this rant entirely in my own head.

What I said on the outside was:

'I'm going out.'

'Where now?' Mum said.

I didn't answer. I just took my jacket from the hook on the back of the door and left.

Business Trouble

I continued to rant in my own head for the whole thirty-five-minute walk to Vicky and Spider's flat.

I was so riled up by the time I arrived that I had to vent immediately, telling them how my parents' idea of a good way to spend a life-changing sum of money was to turn a box room into a study, how they were so uptight and brainwashed by convention that not only were they happy with their own tiny lives, they were trying to do everything in their power to make sure I followed in their boring footsteps.

It has to be said that Vicky and Spider weren't as ruffled by my argument with my parents as I was.

Vicky was lying across the sofa with her feet on the armrest, still in her Madame Violet dress, but without her headscarf this time. Her make-up was smudged around her eyes, making her look somewhere between drunk and distraught. Spider was sitting on the floor with his legs crossed, tearing an old pizza menu into little pieces, rolling them into balls and trying to throw them into an empty pint glass by the wall.

'Sorry, Gracie,' he said glumly. 'Sorry about your parents

and everything. We've just got a few problems of our own right now.'

'Why?' I said. 'Like what?'

'Number one,' Vicky said, swinging her legs off the sofa and sitting upright. 'Spider's old uncle has turned out to be a right tight git and number two – related – we're skint again.'

'How do you mean? We're making loads of money.'

Spider rested his head on his hand. 'We were, until business dried up.'

'Uh huh,' Vicky confirmed. 'Not a single new customer lined up. And now Spider's uncle has decided we have to pay rent on this place!'

'It's not much, to be fair,' Spider said. 'And he needs it to pay for his nurse.'

'Whatever,' Vicky said. 'Still sucks for us.'

'But how can we have no customers?' I said. 'There were so many?'

Vicky just shrugged and slumped down next to me on the sofa.

This was exactly the opposite of what I'd wanted to find when I'd stormed out of home and headed over here. I'd been so fired up, so sure that Mum and Dad were wrong and I was right and that I would show them how I could make my own way in the world, make up my own rules, and still be successful. I felt deflated. Actually, I felt silly.

Spider put some bassy electronic music on the stereo and Vicky lay on the sofa with her head hanging over the arm.

I wanted one of them to say something. I wanted someone to suggest how we could get more customers or come up with a new, ingenious, *fun* business plan to pay for our list of adventures, or even just for one of them to say, 'Beach?'

But they didn't.

We all just sat there, the relentless beat of the music the only sound in the lounge. Spider finished turning the pizza menu into balls and started on an old bus ticket.

Then, at about nine o' clock, the flat's door buzzer sounded.

'You get it,' Spider said to me.

'You get it,' I said to him.

'I'll get it,' Vicky said with a sigh.

I heard her trudge down the stairs, swearing as she stumbled over Spider's trainers on the bottom step. Then I heard voices – Vicky's obviously, and then another female voice – but I couldn't make out what they were saying. A few minutes later Vicky came back up. In fact, she practically bounded.

'Look. At. This,' she said, holding out a small slip of paper.

I took it from her. It was a cheque. For a hundred pounds.

'Mrs C Gunn,' I read aloud. 'Who's that?'

'The old sheila at the door!' she said, her eyes shining. 'She wants – get this – ten sessions with Madame Violet. Ten! And what's ten times fifty, Spidey? Let me hear you say the words!'

'Five hundred,' Spider said, reaching for the cheque to see it for himself.

'You bet it is!' Vicky cried. 'Five hundred big ones!'

'*Ten* sessions,' Spider said, crinkling his nose and shaking his head. 'Why?'

Vicky shrugged and went over to the mirror and started rubbing at her smudged make-up with her sleeve. 'Dead husband. It's been six months and she can't stop thinking about him. Last conversation they had was a row or something; she needs closure. Needs to know he's not angry. Blah blah blah. All mad, obviously.'

'Sounds sad,' Spider said.

I thought it did too, really.

'Yeah, I guess,' Vicky said. 'But remember, all I have to do is say the right thing and we send the old girl away happy. Plus, five hundred pounds, guys! That's like . . . a lot of money.' She turned around and grinned at us.

Spider nodded but he still looked sad. He sighed. 'I guess you're right.'

Mrs C Gunn

Mrs C Gunn's first appointment with Madame Violet was the following day at noon so, naturally, I was instructed to be at the flat to fulfil my usual role of assistant and welcomer.

I was almost late for my shift because as I was striding down the hill I bumped into William again, outside the Age Awareness IT centre.

He was clutching more handwritten letters on his lined notepaper.

'Hello!' he greeted me brightly. 'More letters, you see.' He waved the papers.

I smiled encouragingly. 'Great,' I said. 'Well, good luck.'

I ducked to the side, ready to continue my journey.

'They still need people,' he said. 'To help out. My friend Valerie – I met her here – she's even worse than me. And she doesn't come any more, she's given up. Says computers are too hard. Such a shame! No one to help. You should do it, you know. You'd be so helpful, to old codgers like me.'

I just smiled. 'Maybe,' I said. 'Sorry, I've got to go.'

'Oh, OK,' he said with a note of sadness in his voice. 'Bye then.'

I waved behind me as I jogged down the hill. I hoped I wouldn't be the only person William spoke to today.

I was just about on time to receive Mrs C Gunn for her first appointment at the flat.

When the buzzer sounded and I went down to open the main front door, I found that Mrs C Gunn wasn't really what I imagined.

I'd been expecting a tiny doddery old lady, maybe with one of those plastic headscarves. Definitely with a stick of some sort. I suppose I'd assumed we'd be dealing with someone who wasn't quite all there. Someone who'd witter on about nothing, who wouldn't make much sense.

Mrs C Gunn wasn't like that at all.

Vicky had called her some 'old sheila' but she wasn't *that* old. Older than Mum and Dad but nowhere near as old as Nan had been. She was average in height. She was wearing a flowery blouse that wasn't exactly the kind of thing I'd wear but I wouldn't be surprised if Mum did. She didn't have a headscarf and her hair wasn't even set into a blueish curly perm. It was grey, but in a quite ordinary curly tousled bob. Everything about her seemed quite ordinary really. Not mad or strange or stupid at all.

'Carol Gunn,' she said, in a voice that was quiet and serious but not nervous. 'I have an appointment at twelve, with . . . uh . . . "Madame Violet".' She said the name like she felt a bit silly about having to say it out loud. The way she looked around her before she stepped through the front door – as if she as checking no one was watching – made me wonder if she felt a bit silly about being here at all.

As I led her up the stairs I did all my normal speech about Madame Violet being in her room, preparing herself 'spiritually' for her work. Carol didn't say much. She made a few noises like 'uh-huh' and 'mmm' but the only actual words she said were:

'I can't believe it's come to this.'

Which said a lot about how desperate she was, I thought. I guessed this row she'd had with her husband must've been a big one.

I showed her into the bedroom, then I took a seat on the sofa and waited for her to emerge.

When she did, fifteen minutes later, I started to show her out but she brushed me aside. She seemed distracted. Maybe even a little bit irritated. 'I'm fine to see my own way, thank you. Fine.'

She darted out the door before I could even give her my fake 'spiritual health' warnings about not doing anything emotionally demanding for the rest of the day or talking to anyone else about her private conversations with Madame Violet.

Once she was safely out of the flat, I went into the bedroom. Vicky was sitting in her usual position, cross-legged at the round table on the bed.

She looked shell-shocked.

Difficult Customer

My first instinct was – bizarrely – that somehow Vicky had actually made some kind of contact with Carol's dead husband. That her acting of the role of medium was so effective that she'd genuinely tapped into the afterlife, and the spirit of this old man had started talking to her.

'What's the matter?' I said, hovering in the doorway in case her head started spinning round or she began spewing green slime or something.

'That was intense, man,' she said. She shook her head and rubbed her eyes. 'Intense.'

'Why?' I ventured in now, and took a seat on the end of the bed.

'She, like, really, really wanted to talk to her husband,' Vicky said. 'More than any of the others. And she was on it, you know? *On* it. She was asking me all these questions like "How tall is he?" and "Does he have any distinguishing features?" And I wanted to be like, "Lady, he's your hubby. You tell me." But that's the point, isn't it – she was testing me.'

'So what did you do?' I asked. 'How did you get through it?'

'I blagged it, but only just,' Vicky said. 'I had to keep changing my mind about everything I said and telling her that the signals weren't strong today. I tried to win her over but she was hardcore.

'And the worst bit is, as she was leaving, I said, "I'll see you next time," and she said "Maybe". Maybe! What if she doesn't come back? I need to up my game, kiddo. Otherwise we're throwing those five hundred big ones down the drain.'

When Spider returned half an hour later, Vicky recounted the story of her difficult session to him.

'How did you manage with the others?' he said, as he put the beers away in the fridge. 'You haven't had any trouble convincing anyone else.'

Vicky shrugged. 'I dunno, I just did. Those other guys gave stuff away. They were always mentioning little details or getting excited when I said something right. And they were happy with everything I said. Anything! Not Carol Gunn though. Not Mrs C Gunn. That chick is *tough*. She didn't say anything. I was completely on my own in there. I had to blag like a good 'un.'

Spider frowned as he was thinking and rubbed the back of his head. 'I suppose we need to be more organised.'

'How so?' Vicky asked.

'We need to know more about her,' Spider said. 'We need to do some research. We need to know who she is and who her husband was and more about her whole situation so you can wheel out some genuine facts and get her believing you're really in touch with the other side.'

'So, like . . .' I said, 'we need to spy?'

'Yeah,' Spider said with a helpless shrug. 'If we want the cash, that's what we'll have to do.'

PART 1

During which my three-year-old brother and I form an unlikely private investigation partnership

Google

Naturally, the first thing we did to try to get the measure of Carol Gunn was look her up online.

Spider sat in the corner on Vicky's laptop carrying out search after search, and I did the same from the corner of the sofa on my phone.

Carol Gunn

Carol Gunn Brighton

Carol Gunn husband

Mrs C Gunn husband accident

On and on we went, but it quickly became apparent that Carol Gunn's online profile was virtually non-existent.

'Old people can never get it together to do social media properly,' Vicky moaned.

We had just started to consider the possibility that, despite the name on the cheque, Carol Gunn wasn't called Carol Gunn at all, when we came across the one mention of her online.

It was on the website of a place called Tiny Tigers – a kids' activity centre up near Preston Park. Carol Gunn was listed as a 'Group Assistant' and along with her photo – so we knew we definitely had the right person – there was a short passage saying she had a Level 3 Diploma in childcare.

'Oh great,' Vicky whined. 'What am I supposed to do with that?'

'You can mention children,' Spider suggested. 'It might somehow lead her to reveal something about her own children, if there were any. And that might lead onto her husband . . . I don't know.'

Vicky looked unimpressed.

'We could ask someone else,' I said. 'Now we know where she works. And who she works with.'

Vicky and Spider looked at me and then Vicky nodded slowly.

'Yeah. I get your thinking. Go down there, see what there is to be found out.'

I shrugged. 'I guess.'

'Oh and also,' Vicky said, getting more enthusiastic now and sitting forward on the edge of the sofa. 'You've got your kid brother you can take – the perfect cover story.'

'Me?'

Vicky nodded. 'Yeah, totally, babe. Think about it. I can't go down there, she'll recognise me straight away as Madame Violet and that'll look totally suss. And you can't exactly have some hobo like Spider hanging around a kiddy centre. He'll get arrested. You're a good clean young thing. You go down there with little Teddy –'

'Paddy.'

'Yeah, him. You go down there with him and no one will bat an eyelid.'

318

I thought about this. 'She'll recognise me, though,' I pointed out. 'She's seen me here.'

Vicky dismissed this concern with a wave of her hand. 'Nah, she probably barely looked at you. Anyway, so what if she does? You have a part-time job as an assistant to Madame Violet and you also have a little brother who likes to play with the toys at the kids' centre. Nothing wrong with that. It's got to be you, kiddo, I'm afraid. No two ways about it.'

Tiny Tigers

One perk of being assigned a mission that involved going to Tiny Tigers kids' centre was that it got me back in Mum's good books.

We'd all agreed that I would need to take Paddy with me, as a teenage girl hanging around a play centre for the under-fives would be likely to raise suspicions. When I casually mentioned that I'd like to take Paddy to Tiny Tigers the following day, Mum had looked at me, her head on one side for a moment. Then she'd put her hand on mine and said, 'That would be lovely, Grace. I'd really appreciate it.'

She'd said it in a deliberate, earnest way that I knew was her way of saying, 'I recognise you're trying to make amends for being such a poor member of this family, and I graciously accept your efforts.'

I felt guilty that this was all just part of my plan, but I told myself, what did it matter, really? The end result was the same. Mum and Dad could have an afternoon off looking after Paddy and he'd have a great time rolling around with all the other little kids.

It was five pounds for Paddy to join in a session at Tiny

Tigers. The centre was essentially a big church hall-style room, set up with various stations of children's toys and entertainments – a sandpit, a small paddling pool filled with wooden boats and water wheels, a plastic sheet spread with brushes and powder paints.

I knew which station Paddy would head for as soon as we entered the room.

'Sandwiches!' he cried and delightedly sprinted towards a round plastic table where a man – a member of Tiny Tigers staff, judging from his black-and-orange T-shirt – was handing out pieces of white sliced bread and supervising clumsy children as they slathered them with jam and cut them into triangles.

Paddy clambered onto a plastic stool at the table and said, 'Make sandwiches!' to the Tiny Tigers man.

The man chuckled and handed Paddy a slice of bread and a plastic knife and Paddy immediately got to work, his brow furrowed in concentration. I hovered around just behind him, not quite sure what to do with myself. I thought I should probably help Paddy with his task but there wasn't much room around the small plastic table.

'My name is Paddy,' Paddy told the man, without being asked.

'Cool name,' the man said. 'And who's this?' He nodded up at me, shooting me a knowing grin.

Paddy spun around to see who he was looking at, already forgetting who had accompanied him on his outing.

'Oh, that's my daddy,' Paddy said, inexplicably.

The man laughed loudly.

'I'm his sister,' I clarified. 'Grace.'

The man nodded and patted a plastic stool. 'Take a seat, Grace. I'm Neil.'

I did as I was told and I busied myself passing Paddy spreads and fillings for his sandwich and trying to keep them chiefly on the bread rather than on his clothes.

As Paddy worked, I looked around the stations to check out the other members of Tiny Tigers staff present.

A young blonde woman was helping a boy about Paddy's age wipe blue paint from his forehead. An older woman with a long French plait was helping a mother wrestle her naked toddler back into the clothes that he'd chosen to discard for some reason.

None of them was Carol Gunn. She wasn't here.

This wasn't a huge surprise in itself and, actually, I'd already decided that this would be preferable. It would be easier to try to get the measure of her situation by talking about her rather than to her. I still hadn't formulated an exact plan for how I was going to carry out this conversation though.

I looked at Neil as he was busy putting lids back on jars of peanut butter and jam.

'Does . . .' I began tentatively, 'Does Carol still work here? Carol Gunn?'

The man looked up, surprised. 'Carol? Yeah, she does, yeah. You know her?'

I nodded. I was prepared for this suggestion. 'Yeah. Sort of. Haven't seen her for ages though. She's a friend of my dad's. I just knew she used to work here, that's all.'

The man nodded. 'She does still work here. Officially, anyway. But she's been all over the place since her husband slung his hook.'

I thought that was a strange way of talking about someone's untimely death. Neil misread my perturbed expression as disapproval.

'I mean, sorry, if he was your dad's mate as well or whatever. But he has stitched her up a bit, hasn't he, packing his bags like that.'

Now I was really confused. Packing his bags is surely never a euphemism for death. Were we even talking about the right person?

'Sorry,' I said, shaking my head quickly. If in doubt, play dumb. 'Sorry, I must have heard it wrong from my dad. I just thought her husband had died . . . not sure where I got that from . . . must've got the wrong –'

I stopped because Neil was groaning and rubbing the sides of his head. 'Jesus,' he said. 'That's what's got round, is it? Crikey.'

I just looked at him, confused.

Neil sighed. 'I don't fully know the ins and outs of it myself, but I believe the long and short of it is they had an almighty row, he stormed out, took his little dingy, his little fishing boat out, never came home. So Carol's convinced he's lost at sea. Had the coastguard out and everything, but there's nothing to be found. Meanwhile, a few people reckon they saw him later that night in a bar in Kemptown. She's reported him as missing but police aren't having any of it. The only person who thinks he's actually missing is Carol, but I think – I mean, we all think really – that it's easier for her to believe that he was devoted to her his whole life and is actually dead rather than to think he's run off with some barmaid.'

'What barmaid?'

'Oh, I don't know. Could be anyone. Old Leroy was always at it. Only person who thought he was a saint was Carol. Being honest with you, she's better off without him.'

Tension

The story of Leroy the philandering fisherman put a whole different spin on my mission, and I didn't know quite what to make of it. Neither did Vicky when I took the news back to her.

'Oh Jesus,' she said, sitting down on the sofa and staring into the middle of the room. 'How the bejesus am I supposed to talk to a spirit if there might not even be one?'

I shrugged. 'Well . . . you're pretending anyway, aren't you? You were never actually going to get in touch with Leroy – that's his name by the way, that'll be useful at least – you were never going to pass on any real messages. Carol still thinks he's dead. Or wants to think that, so it's all the same. In fact,' I said, realising something that was probably totally obvious for the first time, 'that's probably why she's so keen to have the sessions with you anyway, isn't it? To get some kind of proof that he's dead. That he hasn't just left her for someone else.'

Vicky nodded thoughtfully. 'Yeah, I guess you're right. And I know he's called Leroy and I've got this boat situation to work with. You done good, kiddo.'

She came over and ruffled my hair then went to her bedroom to work on her latest painting – an unsettling depiction of a circus made up entirely of headless performers.

Later that evening, Spider and Vicky had both had a few beers, the flat was hot and stuffy but no one could be bothered to go out. Vicky was stretched across the sofa and Spider was sitting on the floor with his legs crossed, trying to stick the cracked TV remote back together with superglue. The TV was on – something about decorating houses – but no one was really watching.

'Oh for god's sake,' Spider snapped suddenly, pushing the remote away from him in frustration. 'It won't stick. It's pointless.'

I looked at him, alarmed. Although Vicky was prone to outbursts and temper tantrums, Spider was not.

Vicky turned her head to look at him. 'What's up, Spidey?' she said without much concern. 'What's up your bum?'

Spider sighed. 'I'm too hot,' he said, flapping the bottom of his T-shirt. 'It's stifling in here.'

'Open the window then,' Vicky said, yawning and turning back to her phone.

'It's just,' Spider said, getting up and throwing the window open with force. 'What are we doing? Why are we trapped in this box, watching rubbish on the TV?'

'We're just chilling,' Vicky said. 'Settle down.'

'We're always chilling!' Spider said, throwing his hands up. 'We never do anything.'

Vicky sat up now and looked at him. 'What are you on about, Spidey? We do loads. We go to the beach and we drink beers and you play your bongos and we . . .' She turned to me for support. '. . . We do loads of stuff! Remind him, Gracie.'

'Um . . .' I searched back through the things we'd done, although I realised it had been a while since we'd done anything worth reminiscing about. Ages since we'd done anything from the list. 'Body-boarding,' I said. 'We did that. And we ate a squid. And there was that memorable evening we turned the whole phone book into paper aeroplanes.' I'd been joking, being flippant, but it turned out this was exactly the wrong thing to say.

'Exactly!' Spider said, throwing his hands up. 'You see what I mean? We are literally killing time. We're throwing our lives away. That's what I felt when I was working in that cabin in Solihull. That I was throwing my life away. So that's why I got out. But now here I am, down here, not doing anything better. We're barely making enough money to eat. Unless something changes we're never going to be able to do all those things we've planned. Bucharest. The Taj Mahal. We can all pretend that money doesn't buy you happiness but experiences do. But how are we meant to have experiences without any money?'

'So I'm worse than filing invoices in Solihull? Thanks a bunch, Spider,' Vicky snapped.

Spider sighed. 'I just thought I'd do something with my life. I didn't want to work filing invoices forever, but I did want to achieve something. I still do.' He turned to me. 'I used to think about law, you know. I never talk about it any more but that's where I always saw myself.'

327

Vicky laughed a hard laugh. 'Oh yeah, that's totally you,' she said, her voice heavy with sarcasm. 'All dolled up in a suit, making deals in the boardroom with the city boys. You wouldn't last five minutes, mate.'

'Not that kind of law,' Spider said quietly. 'Immigration, maybe. Human rights.'

Vicky laughed again, loudly this time, like she was genuinely amused. 'Human rights! Oh god, give me strength! What has happened to you, Spider? Who do you think you are!'

Spider didn't even look at her. He crossed the lounge, picking up his keys from the bowl on the shelf on his way out.

We heard him thunder down the stairs, and a few moments later, the front door of the building slammed, making the windows shake.

Further Investigations

On the day of Carol Gunn's next appointment with Madame Violet, I decided to keep my sunglasses on. I knew it would look a little strange, but I also knew I would be returning to Tiny Tigers kids' centre in the not too distant future and it would keep things altogether cleaner if she didn't recognise me as Madame Violet's assistant when I was there.

As before, Carol was quiet and calm. There was certainly nothing about her manner that suggested she was a woman who would prefer to delude herself into thinking her husband was dead rather than admit he'd left her. I led her up the stairs, showed her into Vicky's bedroom and waited.

When Vicky showed her out and Carol once again declined my offer to see her to the front door, I went in to see Vicky at once, keen to hear if the fruits of my investigation had proved helpful.

'How did you go?'

Vicky nodded carefully. 'I think it was OK. I think I pulled it off – the boat stuff didn't go down as well as I hoped but there was a flicker, like she realised I must really be in touch, to know that. I think it's enough to get her back, but we're going to need more. I haven't got anything to say next time. Not enough to keep her interested anyway.'

The following day I returned to Tiny Tigers with Paddy. Mum was delighted that I was putting effort into the family again and Paddy was delighted to be able to go on his first outing with his new companion, a stuffed camel in a blue T-shirt whom, in keeping with his naming conventions, he was calling Big Dick.

Paddy spotted Neil, this time manning the sandpit and, always a sucker for a familiar face, headed over. I scoured the room for any signs of Carol, but once again, she was nowhere to be seen.

'You're back!' Neil said, smiling.

'He just had such a great time the other day!' It wasn't a complete lie; Paddy had been talking incessantly about making sandwiches ever since.

I spent fifteen minutes or so playing in the sand with Paddy. I didn't want to look strange by interrogating Neil immediately. Paddy was anxious to keep Big Dick the camel with him at all times, but was frequently distressed by the amount of sand clinging to his fur, so was causing ripples of giggles to go around the adults present by shouting 'make Big Dick clean now' every few minutes and thrusting him towards me.

When Neil was helping Paddy fill a bucket with sand I felt like I had enough of his attention to try some gentle questioning.

'Carol still not back at work then?' I said, as casually as I could manage.

Neil shook his head, his lips pushed together. He didn't say anything else for a second and I thought I was going to have to prod further, but then he suddenly said, 'She's mad, she's going to lose her job if she's not careful.' He said it quickly, all in one go, like he'd been trying not to say anything but it had just burst out of him.

'Really?' I said. I wasn't sure what else to say, but it turned out that Neil didn't need any more prompting.

'She's almost stopped turning up at work altogether and on the odd occasion she does, she's been acting very strangely, by all accounts. Meanwhile Leroy's probably propping up the bar somewhere or away on the Costa del Sol with whoever. Sandy who works in accounts saw his boat for sale on eBay – so it's hardly wrecked at the bottom of the sea!'

'Did you tell Carol?'

Neil shook his head and held his hands up. 'Oh no, not my place, is it? Let her believe what she wants to believe.'

'Where does she live?' I said, although I wasn't at all sure why. It just occurred to me.

'Live?'

'Yeah. Where does she live again?' Again. As if I knew, I just couldn't quite recall the details.

'Portslade,' he said. 'Near me, actually. Mill Close. I should go and see the old girl, really.'

I nodded but didn't say anything.

'Yeah . . .' he said again. 'I should go and see her.'

A Recruit

It had been so long since I'd rung Til I wasn't totally sure she'd answer.

Luckily she did.

'Yeah?'

'How are you?'

'Yeah.' Til had never been big on small talk.

'Well, anyway, do you want to help me with something? Like a mission type thing?'

'A mission.'

'Yeah. An investigation. I'm trying to find something out.'

'What?'

'I can tell you about it when I see you. Meet me at Portslade station at three?'

'Yeah. OK.' And she was gone.

Til was sitting on a bench outside the station. When she saw me she stood up and ambled over, her hands in her pockets.

'All right?' she said with a nod, but not a smile, so I knew we weren't on completely amiable terms. But she was here, which said a lot. And which was enough for now.

I nodded.

'What's the deal then?'

I had this all worked out. The last thing Til would want to hear was that this had anything to be with my 'new hippy mates' so I had a cover story.

'So you know Ollie?'

'Your brother Ollie?'

I nodded. 'Yeah. I think he's got a girlfriend.'

'Right. So? Who?'

'That's the thing. It's someone weird.'

'Not that girl who wears a snake round her neck in North Laine and always sticks her tongue out when she seems him?'

'Oh. No. Not her. Weirder though, in a way. There's this kids' play centre that we take Paddy to sometimes, and there's this woman who works there. I think it might be her.'

'So? So ask him? Does it matter?'

'He wouldn't tell us. Because it's . . . it's weird.'

'Huh? What is?'

'The woman. She's like sixty, Til! She's called Carol and she's old enough to be his grandmother!'

Til made a face. 'Ew. That's so gross.'

'Exactly. But Ollie won't tell us the truth, so we're here, on her road, to ask her ourselves.'

Til stopped and looked at the houses around us. 'What? Are you insane?'

'No. What? Why?'

'You can't just march up to some old woman and ask her if she's doing your brother.'

'We're not going to march anywhere. I have a plan.'

Til looked at me. 'Why does it matter anyway? He's a big boy. Let him do what he wants.'

I sighed. 'Til, Ollie is not a big anything. He's a man-child. And she is a grown woman. She's grooming him! If you had a brother, you'd understand.'

I threw this line in to let Til know that no matter how illogical the whole scheme seemed, it was fuelled by a mystical fraternal concern that she could never fully appreciate without experiencing herself. It seemed to work, just.

Til still looked more than a little dubious but she said, 'So what's the plan?'

I reached into my rucksack and pulled out a clipboard with a form clipped to it.

'How do you want to pay your council tax?' Til read aloud from the top.

'Oh, it's just a dummy form. I just picked it up. You don't really use that. It's just a prop.'

'A prop for what?'

'Market research. You're carrying out door-to-door market research so you need to ask her a few questions. Market researchers can get away with asking all kinds of rubbish. So say you're from the TV people or something, about viewing habits, then ask her the basics – age, job and all that. Then you can get to the 'Single/Married/Other' bit. So pay special attention to that bit. Then basically improvise from there. Just try to find out as much as you can about her love li—'

'Woah,' Til said, holding her hand up to stop me mid-flow.

'Why am I doing all this? What are you doing?'

'Well, I can't do it, can I? She's seen me, up at the centre with Paddy.'

Til sighed. 'Right, fine. Whatever. Jesus. Why do I do this stuff for you?'

Market Research

I'd already established which house was Carol's, which was a really quite simple case of searching the electoral roll as I already had her name, her husband's name and her road name. I waited at the end of the road, a good way away from the house, partly to avoid being spotted lurking by Carol, but also so I wouldn't put Til off her acting.

After five minutes I started looking towards the house, expecting to see Til heading my way, but there was no sign of her. I couldn't see the front door itself, so I had to assume she was still going through her questions.

After fifteen minutes, I started to worry that something was wrong. Initially, just that Til had changed her mind, had got in a strop about being used and had stormed off home without bothering to let me know. Then my worries moved on and started to conjure up more dramatic scenarios. Carol was possibly unhinged – could she have attacked Til? Was Leroy in there? Could he have attacked Til?

Til had been gone twenty minutes when she finally reappeared from around the corner.

'Jesus,' she said, looking exhausted. She shook her head. 'Jesus.'

'What? What happened? Did you do the questions?'

Til shook her head and sat down on the wall. I sat beside her.

'I didn't even say I was doing market research. I didn't even start that.'

'What? Why?'

'When she opened the door, she said, "You here about the sale?" and I was going to say no, but then I thought, go with it, you know? Might be a bit more believable than your market research idea – which, no offence, was pretty dodgy. So I went in, not really knowing what kind of sale it was, but getting ready to be interested in whatever she had going, and then I saw straight away, she had *everything* going.

'Like, all her stuff was priced up. TV, forty-five quid. Sofas, hundred quid each. You could see a lot of it was already gone because some rooms were pretty empty, but like . . . everything, man. Everything was for sale. Mugs, hanging from the dresser, fifty pence each. Even this mug with her grandkids' faces on it! Every little thing.

'So anyway, I said something like, "Wow, you're really having a clear out," and she nodded the smallest, saddest nod you ever saw and said, "Money's tight." And I thought that was it, but then she added, "Since my husband died." So I was like, oh god, what am I supposed to say to that, so I just said, "Oh I'm sorry," and I've still got your whole private investigation thing in my head, so I'm trying to work out how I can ask her if she's got a new boyfriend and if he

337

happens to be a man-child called Ollie but then she starts talking again and she says, "The worst part is he went missing in an accident at sea so getting a death certificate is proving next to impossible and no death certificate means no insurance pay-out so as well as finding myself on my own at the age of sixty-three I've got these bills and –" And then she sort of stopped like she realised she was going off on one, but to be honest I'd heard enough. I mean, I don't know if it was a sales strategy or whatever but it worked, man! Look at all this stuff!'

Til opened her bag and I peered in. Two mugs, a paperweight, a framed embroidery of a cow riding a bike and a DVD called *Gentle Summer Workout*.

'Anyway, it was properly awkward, obviously, but somehow – god knows I'm a good friend to you – somehow I managed to be like, "And you haven't met another partner?" and she nearly had a breakdown! Went on about how she could never look at another man again! If she was acting it was good. I can't see it, Grace. I seriously can't see her going out with Ollie. That is too, too bizarre.'

And right there, just then, I suddenly felt it. I felt that this was not fun any more. I was looking at the sad collection of objects that Carol was having to sell – the paperweight, the cow on the bike, the mugs, for god's sake – lying there in Til's bag, all for a few pathetic pounds, which would end up in Vicky's pocket eventually anyway.

This was not fun any more.

Carol Gunn, whoever she was, whoever or wherever her husband was, was obviously going through some stuff, to put it mildly. And we were hounding her and messing with her head and taking money that she clearly didn't have.

This wasn't a laugh, was it. This wasn't living for the moment.

Conscience

'Oh god,' I said.

'I know,' Til said.

'No, but really. Like really oh god.'

Til gave me a questioning look and I looked at her with her bag full of random things she'd bought to try to help Carol Gunn and to try to help me when I'd given her a half-baked implausible mission – and I suddenly realised, I missed her. And I'd lied to her for what? To make some cash so I could keep eating frozen chips from a mixing bowl on the floor of Vicky and Spider's flat? So I could pretend that Mum and Dad would let me go travelling around Europe with two people I'd only just met? I had a sudden impulse to tell Til everything. To empty myself of it all.

So I did.

I told her about our list, of all the things we'd already done, but all the things I still wanted to do. I explained how we'd run out of money, and how we'd set up the Madame Violet Verano business to make some extra.

Til just looked at me, her expression set to one I was more than familiar with:

Bemused. Amused. Incredulous but resigned. A look that said 'you are so weird, Gracie'.

And then I told her how Carol Gunn fitted into the plan.

And then her expression changed. Her face no longer said, 'you are so weird, Gracie'. Her face now said, 'you disgust me'.

'That's horrible,' she said quietly.

'I know.'

'You should have seen her in there, man. A mess.'

'I know.'

Then Til stood up. She looked at me and she said, 'Who even are you? I don't know you any more.'

This was a line so clichéd, so borrowed from soaps and Hollywood that if anyone else had said it, or if the circumstances had been different, Til would have rolled her eyes and sniggered. But not now. She either hadn't noticed or didn't care. She was too wound up. Too appalled.

'I'm going home now,' she said.

'OK.'

And she went.

The Truth

It was a forty-minute walk to the flat from Carol's house, and by the time I arrived I was clear on what I wanted to say.

I felt sure they too would realise. They'd be quiet, maybe. Sheepish. Ashamed.

I'd recounted exactly what had happened in Mill Close. Carol's grief. Her financial hardship. The fact she was selling off mugs with her grandchildren's faces on them for fifty pence. I'd told the story well, I thought. I'd even got a bit emotional about it.

'Stupid cow,' Vicky said. She was laughing but not smiling. She was drunk.

I blinked, surprised. Vicky had always been cutting. I had known her to say harsh things, but this seemed more than cutting. This seemed cruel.

'I –' I stopped. I wasn't sure what I wanted to say. I looked at Spider. I felt sure he at least would support me.

He wasn't looking at me. He was looking out the window. He too had a beer can in his hand.

'It's up to her, I guess,' he said flatly. 'Can't save people if they're mental.'

'Tell you what, though,' Vicky said, putting her foot up on the sofa and starting to paint her toenails. 'This is gold, some of this stuff. You can tell me all about the gear she's got for sale and I can use that to really get to her. If I can throw in a little detail about her plates with the blue daisies or whatever, that will show her I'm legit. She'll be all over it.'

'No,' I said, more loudly than I'd expected. 'No.'

'You what, mate?' Vicky looked up at me.

'I don't want you to do that.'

Vicky laughed. 'You sound about six years old, Gracie baby.'

But I didn't laugh. 'I think you should stop now. She's had enough. I've had enough, actually.'

Vicky yawned, deliberately. 'You know where the door is, kiddo.'

'I'm going to tell her. If you don't stop, I'll tell her who you really are.'

Spider looked at me then, and he looked at Vicky, but she didn't look up. She carried on painting her toenails. I thought she wasn't going to reply at all, but then suddenly she put her foot down on the floor, and carefully put the top back on her nail varnish.

'You know what I think, kiddo,' she said in a voice that was bright and cheerful but in a way that was so false it was almost menacing. 'I think this little arrangement has run its course, you know? You're cute and dumb and it's been fun, but the thing is, you can't have it all one way. You're happy to run around with us all summer, watching our TV, eating our food, but when it comes to the cold, hard reality of where the cash is going to come from, you bottle it.

'And it's fine, because you know what? That's just your age showing. That's just your immaturity. You can't help it. You'll grow up, one day, at some point. But right now, Spidey and I have done enough babysitting. You go back home to Mummy and Daddy and back to school and your exams and then you can get some nice cosy job in an office. Do your nine to five, go home to your little semi in the 'burbs and I'm sure you'll be just fine.'

I looked at her, tears in my eyes. I hated her. I really felt like I hated her.

Spider was still looking out the window, acting as if no one had said anything. He took a drag on his cigarette. He looked exhausted, I could see that now. Thin and tired and miserable.

There didn't seem to be anything else to say. I turned and went down the stairs and out of the building. I didn't even bother to slam the door.

I hadn't stormed out. I'd just left.

It was over.

As I walked, heading east along Western Road, I took my phone out of my pocket. I had notifications – likes and replies from strangers to some tweet I'd posted about a drunk man on my train – but no messages. Nothing from anyone I actually knew. Nothing from anyone who actually knew me.

I thought Til might have sent me something. Most likely a reiteration of her disgust, but a small hopeful part of me thought she might have calmed down, and want to talk about it at least.

I thought Mum might have messaged me to ask me to pick up something from the shops or to see if I'd be in for dinner.

But nothing.

My family were annoyed with me. My one real friend was annoyed with me. My new friends had turned out to not be friends at all.

I arrived at the top of Albion Hill. I was nearly home, but I didn't want to be. I wouldn't be able to act normal and Mum would be snappy or disappointed and I'd be snappy and sullen back and everything would be even worse.

Instead, I crossed the road and headed into Queen's Park. I walked around aimlessly for a while until I realised I was crying. Like properly crying. I sat down, my back against a tree. I only realised then that it was the exact spot I'd met Vicky and Spider.

Suddenly, everything felt hopeless.

I couldn't think of one single thing I wanted to do. I couldn't even think of something I wanted to do then and there, with the rest of that warm summer evening, let alone what I was going to do with the rest of my life. There was just over a week until I was due back at school, expected to be full of enthusiasm and energy and dedication for the four A levels I'd persuaded them to let me do. The thought made me feel sick.

'Grace? What's going on?'

I looked up.

It was Sarah.

PART 8

During which I realise a number of people, myself included, are not that great

Rescue

'Nothing,' I said automatically, wiping my face with my sleeve. I was torn between the sudden realisation that there was no one I wanted to see more right at that moment, and being painfully aware how horrific I must have looked.

'Right. OK,' Sarah said, her head on one side. 'Um . . . you sure about that?'

'I'm fine,' I said. I over-emphasised it. It sounded aggressive.

'OK,' she said again. 'Right. OK. I'll go then.'

She hovered for a moment, obviously waiting for me to change my mind but I didn't say anything. I didn't know what to say.

She left and I watched her go. I stared at her back, willing her to turn around but she didn't.

I was utterly alone.

I got up and went over to the children's play park. I sat on a swing. I'd stopped crying now. I felt numb. Hopeless and numb.

'Jesus.'

I looked up.

'I've been looking for you for properly ages, what are you doing hanging round in here?'

Til.

'I – why have you been looking for me?'

'Sarah messaged me. Said you're having some kind of nervous breakdown in the park so I thought I should get up here and see what you've been up to now.'

I didn't say anything. She sat down on the swing beside me.

'So what is it? What you been blubbing about?'

'I haven't.' I didn't even know why I was lying.

'Not what Sarah said. And not what the state of your face says either, to be honest.' She passed me a tissue. 'Clean yourself up, girl.'

I did as I was told.

'I tried to tell them,' I said. 'About Carol. About her selling everything.'

'Right.'

'But . . .'

'But they weren't overcome with sympathy for the desperate wannabe widow?'

I shook my head.

'No offence, Gracie, but I think your mates Vicky and Spiderman or whatever might be idiots.'

I nodded and looked down at my hands.

'And, like, also no offence, but you've not exactly been that great either, lately. Like, I know you wanted someone to do your list with or whatever but . . .'

She trailed off. I just nodded again. She was right. I wasn't that great.

350

'I just . . . freaked out,' I said quietly. 'I just thought, I don't know if I can do it. Keep ticking days off my calendar, planning every hour out according to how many pages I can read or essays I can write in one session with just a five-minute break to eat "brain food" and walk around the block to look forward to.'

'I know.'

'And you were getting so into your plumbing and even Ollie's going back to college now and I felt like I was the only person in the world who could see sense, and, like, Vicky and Spider were sent to me, like some kind of sign . . . and I don't know. I just didn't want to think. About anything. I just wanted to *do*. I wanted to live. Just for the very moment.'

'I know. I know you did. It's all you've been banging on about for weeks.' She said it with a grin and so I smiled too. 'Thing is though, Gracie. Yeah, you want to live for the moment. I get that. But then at some point, the future will be the moment. The future will become the present. The future present.'

'Sounds like something we have to learn in French.'

'I just mean –'

'Yeah, I know,' I sighed. 'I can't escape the future by pretending it's not going to happen.'

'Nah. It's more like . . . you can do both. You have to live for the present and the future.'

'Great,' I said miserably. 'Easy. Why not bring some Victorian bonnets along for the ride and we can try to live for the past too, go for a totally unachievable triumvirate?'

'It's like a balance, isn't it? Why do you have to be so

extreme, man? Can't you do a *bit* of study and a *bit* of bungee jumping or whatever? A bit of now, a bit of future. Why is it all-or-nothing?'

I shrugged. 'I don't know,' I said quietly. 'I got carried away.'

'You know the other thing though, Gracie – there's living for the moment and there's having fun . . . and then there's just being an idiot. Like a mean idiot, actually.'

I sighed. Til certainly knew how to kick a person when they were down.

'I'm sorry, man, but cruel to be kind and all that. You can have fun without ditching your mates. You can have fun without being an a-hole to your mum. You can have fun without ripping off old ladies with mental health issues.'

I nodded.

'And you know what else? You can have fun without caring so much about what strangers on the internet think of you too.'

I nodded again.

Then I took out my phone. I typed something out. I hit Tweet.

Til looked at me questioningly, and took out her own phone. '"I, Grace Dart, am a massive twat",' she read aloud. 'Awesome.' She laughed. 'Oh, look a retweet already. Your people clearly agree.'

I smiled.

'It was also to do with my nan, you know,' I said. 'Her letter at her funeral. I kept thinking it was like it was what she wanted me to do.'

'Oh, yeah course,' Til said, nodding seriously. 'I forgot about the bit in her letter where she told you to ditch your best mate and to saddle yourself to some pointless hippies. Let me just check where she said that . . .'

'I don't mean –' I started, but I stopped when I saw Til take a sheet of paper out of her bag and unfold it. 'Is that it there? Is that Nan's letter?'

Til nodded and handed me the piece of paper.

'Why do you have it?'

Til shrugged. 'Got a copy off the celebrant. I just liked it. I keep it with me. I look at it sometimes.'

The thought of grumpy, sarcastic, cynical Til doing something as sentimental as carrying around the deathbed advice of my rude, curmudgeonly, funny nan made me feel emotional all over again.

I read over the letter. I couldn't believe I hadn't thought of asking for a copy myself.

'Good old Nan,' I said quietly.

'Good old Hairy-Face Man,' Til agreed.

We both laughed.

'You know one thing you haven't completely blown?'

'Just one?'

'Just one,' Til confirmed. 'But a good one. Sarah. She still asks about you.'

'Really?' Even hearing her name still made me feel funny.

Til nodded. 'You should talk to her.'

I sighed. 'There are probably a lot of things I should do.'

PART 9

During which I make a new, altogether more important, list and begin work on it at once

A New List

It had been eighteen hours since Til had found me on the swings in Queen's Park. I folded my new list and put it into my pocket. It was time to put it into action.

The first thing was the one I was least looking forward to, but it was also one of the most important. It was something I had to do before I did anything else:

1. Tell Carol Gunn the truth

As I stood outside her house on Mill Close I saw that already the front garden was sparser that it had been the day before.

The pots of hydrangeas along the front wall had gone. The blind from the front window had gone. The little blue plaque bearing her house number had gone. This woman really was selling off everything.

I had no idea how she planned to live once she'd raised her money to give to Vicky. She couldn't sleep on the bare floorboards, could she? Drink out of an old margarine tub? I was worried she hadn't really thought this through. Perhaps that was why I was there.

She recognised me as soon as she opened the door.

'What's happened?' she said, her eyes wide. 'Has something come through, a message?'

'No.' I shook my head. 'It's nothing like that. Can I come in?'

I didn't want to go in at all really – partly because I didn't want to be trapped on the inside while I had to confess to a potentially unhinged woman that I'd played a central role in defrauding her during a difficult time in her life, but also because I didn't want to see the devastation of her home in full-colour detail. But it seemed the right thing to do, if I was going to do this properly.

'It is about Madame Violet . . . about Vicky, but it's not what you think.'

She frowned and rubbed her head. Then she sat down in a plastic garden chair, now the only item of furniture in her living room.

'Who's Vicky?'

So I told her. I tried to justify it, how it had started off as a bit of fun, and a way to make some harmless extra money.

'We didn't think people really believed in that stuff,' I said before immediately realising this was the worst thing I could have said.

I suppose I thought she'd be furious and indignant. I suppose I was thinking of her as a person who had been charged for a service by someone who had no intention of delivering it. I was thinking of her as a disgruntled customer. But of course, that wasn't how it was really. She hadn't been conned into paying for a luxury holiday apartment only to find herself crammed into a studio overlooking a building site. This went deeper than that.

She started crying. Not huge wailing sobs, just silent tears running down her cheeks. I almost couldn't look.

'I've been such a fool,' she said quietly.

'No,' I said. 'It's not your fault. It was us. Vicky.'

'He's not even dead, is he. He just doesn't want me any more.'

She cried some more, and I put my hand on hers. I didn't know if that was the right thing to do but she didn't move away, so we stayed like that for a while.

I stood up. There didn't seem to be anything else to say.

'You can have your money back, obviously.' I reached into my pocket and put the cheque she'd given us on the floor, as there was nowhere else to leave it. I was also still carrying around some of our other takings, around sixty pounds in cash, so I left that there too. Compensation, I suppose.

And then I left.

2. Talk to Sarah

I hadn't been inside the library since the day I'd told Sarah I had the tickets I didn't actually have, but I still had her shift pattern committed to memory, so unless things had changed, I knew she'd be there.

I couldn't see her anywhere at first, and so I panicked. It had been weeks after all. Maybe things *had* changed. Maybe her shift pattern was different or maybe she'd left the library altogether to focus on her A levels and then maybe she'd moved away from Brighton altogether and I would never see her aga—

'Oh, hey, Grace.' She appeared next to me. She was wearing a badge on a cord round her neck with her photo and name on it. She saw me looking. 'New security thing,' she explained.

I nodded.

'Everything OK now?' she said carefully. 'You OK, I mean?'

'Yeah,' I said, cringing at the thought of how mad I must've looked sobbing alone under a tree in Queen's Park. 'Sorry, bad day . . . or something.'

She just nodded and gave me a tight smile. She was being guarded, I could tell. She would be polite to me but no more than that. She headed over towards the Media Centre pushing her trolley of books.

'I just wanted to say . . .' I called after her.

She stopped and turned around. What did I want to say? I suddenly wasn't sure.

'I'm not with her. Vicky. The Australian.'

Sarah just looked at me.

'She's not even nice. I think she's weird, maybe, actually. So I mean, we're not friends any more, even. We broke up. As friends I mean! That's all.'

Sarah scrunched up her nose and put her head on one side. Then she shrugged. 'OK,' she said. 'Thanks for . . . keeping me updated, I guess?'

She carried on across the library. I followed her again. This was going terribly.

'Look, Sarah. I'm sorry. I've been an idiot. Til told me that's how I've been. Not that I needed to be told because I had actually worked it out for myself but I'm still sorry about it. I think I just had a crisis. Or a meltdown or something. I went mad from revision.'

Sarah laughed, and started looking at labels on the spines of the books. 'I can understand that.'

I nodded. 'So if you wanted to, like, do something? Again? Maybe I could actually get tickets to . . . whatever this time.'

Sarah nodded slowly. 'OK. Sure. Maybe. Probably. I'll text you.'

'OK,' I said. I breathed out. 'OK.'

I think that was the best I could do for now.

Onwards.

3. Make it up to Til

Podrick's Hardware Store was on the way to Til's flat. I hadn't been there for years, since I was a little kid, when Ollie and I would use brooms as light sabres while Mum browsed the bathroom sealants.

I stood in the plumbing section and scanned the array of plastic pipes and putties and nuts and chains.

'Can I help you there?' a middle-aged man in a blue Podrick's T-shirt said.

'Um . . . maybe. If you were training to be a plumber and you wanted a really nice tool, like something special, what would be good?'

The man thought for a moment. 'A special plumbing tool, eh? Present for Dad, is it?'

'Something like that.'

He reached up and took something from a high shelf.

'This is pretty snazzy,' he said. 'It's a basin wrench but it's more than just a basin wrench. You can do the whole lot with that – fit TRV valves, basin nuts, balance your radiators. And it's nickel plated, too.'

I looked at the strange-shaped smooth metal object. 'It sounds wonderful,' I told the man. It certainly looked shiny anyway.

'What is it?' Til said when I handed her the bag and she pulled out the tool.

'A basin wrench,' I explained. 'You can fit TRV valves and do basin nuts and balance radiators. It's nickel plated.'

'Do what to basin nuts?'

'Um, not sure. Whatever you do to nuts?'

Til laughed. 'OK. Cool. It's great, I think. I guess I'll find out soon enough. So, thanks, obviously. Thanks for getting it for me.'

I shrugged. 'That's OK. It's to say sorry. About, you know . . .'

'Being a twat.'

'Yeah. That.'

'OK,' she said. 'Over it, to be honest.'

'Cool. So we're, like, friends again?'

Til rolled her eyes and flopped down on her bed. 'Jesus, are you eight?'

But she was smiling.

4. Apologise to Mum and Dad

'You've been quiet, love. This morning, and yesterday.' Mum was using a teaspoon to chip away at the melted cheese on the bottom of the grill. I was boiling the kettle and staring at nothing.

'I've been having an existential crisis.'

Mum pulled her head out of the grill and looked at me. 'Oh goodness!' she said. 'This morning?'

I shook my head. 'All summer. Since we got back from Spain.'

'Oh, OK,' Mum said, frowning.

'It's why I've been . . . difficult,' I said.

Mum just nodded. I noticed she didn't jump to disagree.

'In fact, where's Dad? I want to do this properly.'

'He's making the bed. Shall I call him? Do what properly? Do you have another announcement? Is it a girl?'

'No, it's not a girl! But yes, get Dad. And Ollie too. I want to call a family meeting.'

'Goodness,' Mum said again, putting down the teaspoon. 'How official. Paddy?'

I nodded and took a seat at the head of the kitchen table. 'Yes, yes. Paddy too. And Dick and Big Dick and anyone else who wants to come.'

A few minutes later my parents and brothers were sitting around the table. Paddy had duly brought both Dick and Big Dick along. He had painted Big Dick's mouth with Mum's red lipstick in honour of the occasion.

Ollie had a notepad in front of him.

'What are you doing?' I said.

'Taking minutes,' he said.

'Why?'

'It's a meeting, isn't it? This is how you have a meeting. Actually, wait.' He got up and put four chocolate digestives on a plate in the middle of the table. 'You always have biscuits at a meeting. On a plate, not in a packet.'

'Only four though?' Dad said. 'Seems a bit mean. Especially when there are five of us.'

Ollie shrugged. 'No one eats the biscuits though. That's not the point. Everyone just looks at them.'

'Right, yes. Anyway –' I began.

'Is there an agenda?' Ollie said. 'It's important to have clear objectives for a meeting so that we don't drift off topic.'

'No!' I said. '*You're* drifting off topic. Shut up.'

Ollie pulled a face of mock innocence. 'Oh. So sorry. What is the topic?'

'The topic is my apology.'

'Apology for what?' Dad said, reaching for a biscuit. 'Sorry, Ol. I'm going to eat one. I know it's against protocol but I'm a growing boy.'

'Apology for my existential crisis and resultant poor form.'

'Yeah, you have been a total pain in the bum,' Ollie said.

'Bum,' Paddy whispered to Big Dick.

'Yeah, all right. Fine,' I said. 'But I was just trying to . . . I don't know. I got worried. About life and death and doing the right things and having fun.'

'Deep,' Ollie said.

'Quite,' Mum said. 'No wonder you've been feeling out of sorts with all that on your mind.'

I sighed. 'I just don't think I want to go back to school. I literally cannot bear the idea.'

'Right,' Mum said. 'Right, OK. Well, OK. So don't.'

'What?'

'You're sixteen. You don't have to go back to school, necessarily. You have to do something, but there are other options.'

'But, you always said . . . you said work hard at school and do my best and . . . all of that stuff.'

Mum nodded and reached for a biscuit. 'Well, yes. We want you to reach your potential and have options but we didn't want to give you an existential crisis. I don't think we've ever put pressure on you. Have we?'

I thought about this. 'No, I suppose not.'

But I'd definitely felt the pressure. Where had it come from? Had I invented it? Had I let myself go mad, succumbing to an outside force that didn't even exist?

'So what are you going to do? Ollie said, taking his phone out of his pocket and reading a text. He was clearly losing interest in proceedings.

'I don't know,' I said quietly.

Which brought me to the last item on my list. The most difficult one of all.

5. Decide what to do with the rest of my life

'Do you want to get a job?' Mum said. 'You'd be starting at the bottom but you could work your way up, I suppose. Karen's boy, Luke, started as a cashier in the bank and now he's a . . . I don't know . . . relationship manager or something. He wears a nice shirt every day anyway. And he has a sign on his desk, a gold one with his name engraved. Karen's told me about it four times.'

'I don't know,' I said again. 'I don't think so. I mean, it's not that I think I know everything –'

'Just most things?' Ollie raised one eyebrow.

'No! It's just that I don't want to be bored and stressed and miserable for the next two years just so I can do a job that makes me bored and stressed and miserable.'

'That wouldn't be ideal,' Dad conceded.

'Come to college with me,' Ollie said.

This was actually the idea that I kept coming back to. It was like Til had said: I needed to find a compromise.

'Yes. I think I might want to do that, actually. I think that might be OK.'

Ollie laughed. 'You're joking? You've spent the whole summer going off the rails and have gathered us here for a family meeting to say you want to go to college instead of sixth form. Biggest anti-climax ever.'

'Oliver!' Dad said. 'Sometimes these things come full circle. And it's good that you want to go to college. What do you want to do?'

We talked some more and agreed that not only did I not know what I was going to do after college, I didn't want to know. Everything could be different in two years' time. It was like what Ollie had said to me the day he'd told me about his Music Production course: sometimes it was nice to enjoy the process, rather than worrying about the result.

I wanted to enjoy the next two years, not just wait for them to be over.

In the end, Mum and I went down to the college admissions office and had a long discussion about my options, and given that it was catastrophically late to be having this change of heart, I was well aware I might have to wait a year to be allowed in at all. After looking at the prospectus and the timetabling that had already been arranged and thinking about what I would actually be interested in, I settled on three subjects:

> Art: because it was fun.
> Business Studies: because despite the dubious morals of the endeavour, I had quite enjoyed the creative challenge of setting up Madame Violet's studio.
> Psychology: so next time I had an existential crisis I might be better equipped to deal with it.

It turned out to be quite the summer of existential crises, because along with me going off the rails and Ollie deciding that his future – his immediate future, anyway – lay in music production, Dad had also decided to make some changes.

After a few weeks of nerve-wracking waiting to hear whether he was going to be made redundant, he eventually found out that his job was safe. But, the news didn't please him as much as he thought.

'I'd sort of got used to the idea of a fresh start,' he explained. 'I'd already looked into becoming a sailing instructor at the marina. And now . . . I don't know.'

Dad talked it over with Mum and he agreed to drop down to three days a week in his computer job, and for the other two, he'd give the sailing a proper shot.

'If it doesn't work out, I can always go back up to full time,' he explained. 'I just don't want to waste all day every day doing something I hate.'

'Hey, you don't need to justify it to me, Dad,' I said. 'I totally get it.'

Freshers

On the Friday that marked the end of the first week at college, some boys from the year above arranged a kind of informal freshers-style drinks on the beach.

I headed down with Til. After a difficult summer friendship-wise, it felt like she and I were getting back on track, and far from being annoyed that I was encroaching on her territory by deciding to join her at college, she said she was pleased. When I'd gone to see her to let her know my change of plans, she admitted that she too had been rethinking her options. Now, alongside her plumbing NVQ she was studying for a psychology A level, so we'd be in the same class.

She'd come over all coy when she'd told me. Sheepish even.

'I know I'm not exactly the academic one and I didn't think I was into all that psychobabble stuff anyway, but I've been reading bits lately on the internet about why Mum is such a fruit loop and it's kind of interesting. It would be nice to know what's what, you know?'

As we arrived on the beach and slung our jackets down in the centre of one of the little circles of people that were dotted over the stones, I spotted Sarah, sitting cross-legged with a few people from her year. She'd had her hair cut into a neat bob. She looked nice. It was nice, to see her there, at the same event as me. I liked the idea that we shared something now, that we were part of the same community.

I had had to check – to double-check with myself, and with Til – that my decision to ditch school in favour of college was nothing to do with Sarah's attendance at the latter. That would not have been an acceptable reason to alter my life course. I think I passed the check, though. It wasn't to do with her, not really. Not at all, actually. But that didn't change the fact that I spent much of each day half expecting – half hoping – to bump into her, in the canteen, in the corridor. Anywhere, really.

I'd definitely hoped she'd be there that evening.

I think she must have sensed me looking at her, because she looked up and smiled. But then she turned back to her conversation and I sat down thinking that was it. That was all the interaction I was going to get. A smile. I'd spent twenty minutes deciding what T-shirt to wear for a smile.

But then, ten or fifteen minutes later, I saw her stand up and move away from her little group and head over to where Til and I were sitting.

'Hey,' she said, crouching down next to us. 'I thought I'd seen you around college.'

I nodded. 'Yeah.' That was it. That was all I could think to say.

Til got up and excused herself. Sarah sat down properly, crossing her legs. 'You should've said you were coming tonight. I didn't realise.'

'Well, you said you'd text and so I didn't want to text you and I didn't think you'd actually be that interested anyway – that I was coming here, I mean – but then you didn't text me at all and so . . . I don't know.' It came out in a rush. An unrestrained gush of words.

Sarah laughed. 'Beautifully put.'

I smiled.

'I did want to text,' she said slowly 'But . . .' She trailed off.

'But just not enough to actually do it?' I suggested. I'd meant it as a joke but I'd delivered it like a criticism and Sarah looked wounded.

'Sorry,' I said.

She sighed. 'The thing is, Grace, you kind of made me feel like an idiot. I said "I like you" and then next thing I know you're snogging some Australian.'

I nodded sadly. 'I was the idiot. Not you.'

'Yes,' Sarah agreed. 'Perhaps.'

I didn't know what to say to this. I'd messed it all up. And I'd said sorry but there was nothing else I could do about it. I felt sad.

Sarah stretched her legs out in front of her and leant back on her elbows. 'You want to come to Alton Towers?' she said suddenly.

I looked at her. 'What? Now?'

She laughed. 'No. Next weekend. For my birthday. Johnny's driving.' She nodded over towards a boy with tattoos down one arm who I vaguely recognised from college.

I shrugged and smiled. 'OK,' I said. 'Sure. Sounds good.'

'Great,' she said. 'I'll text you.'

I looked at her. She laughed. 'No, I mean I will actually text you.'

I smiled and Sarah kissed me.

It was only on the cheek but it was enough for Til to raise her eyebrows from where she was sitting a few metres away and for a drunk man who was part of a stag party to let out a small cheer.

Spider

On the way home that night, I passed the part of the beach outside Bar Ten where I'd spent so many evenings that summer with Vicky and Spider. I don't know why but I couldn't help scanning the crowd for them. It was just strange, I think, how quickly and comprehensively they had both entered and left my life.

I didn't see them. I didn't think they were there. They'd be in the flat probably, watching pointless television and drinking beers and bickering.

Then I heard a voice.

'Grace?'

Spider.

I looked at him. He looked tired. I didn't say anything.

'How are you?' he said.

I shrugged. 'Yeah, fine.' I was cold. My tone was unfriendly; I knew it was. It was deliberate. He hadn't actively participated when Vicky had been laying into me but neither had he raised any objections or done anything to stop it.

'I'm sorry,' he said quietly. 'Really sorry.'

'Right,' I said. 'OK.' I wasn't going to make it easy for him.

'You were right,' he said.

'About what?'

'Everything. What we were doing. I wanted to tell that woman – Carol – but I didn't know how to find her –'

'I sorted it.'

He looked surprised. 'Oh, OK. Thanks, then.'

We were quiet again.

'Vicky . . . she's got issues,' he went on.

'Yep.' No arguments from me there.

'She's gone.'

'Where?'

Spider shrugged. 'I kicked her out. It's my flat. My uncle's, anyway. So I don't know now. Australia? London? I want to get my life together. My uncle died last week. I hadn't been bothered to see him. Not for ages. That isn't me. It wasn't before, at least. I'm a good person, Grace.'

'What does that mean?'

'I want to help people. Do something. I'm going to train. As something. Maybe law. I haven't decided.'

'OK. Well, good luck.'

'Same to you, Grace. Good luck. I think you're going to be great. Whatever you do, you'll be great at it.' He gave me a wide smile, but there were tears in his eyes.

The Future

I did a lot of things that summer that I wasn't proud of, but once I started to make amends for those things, I realised that it hadn't been a total disaster.

There had been plenty of moments that I'd enjoyed and, more importantly, some moments that I would always be grateful for.

Some of these were obvious.

Spending some of the last days of Nan's life with her in Paris was something I'd never forget. Talking to Ollie – properly talking – about our futures and our lives meant that we got on better now than we ever had, although we still argued weekly, if not daily.

Some bits hadn't necessarily been enjoyable, but I was still glad I'd done them, in the end.

Having a go on Rush was certainly an experience.

It was good to be able to say I'd tried frogs' legs.

Til and I still laughed about our afternoon on Nobby and Petal.

One thing that I was surprised about enjoying though, was my twenty minutes in the Age Awareness UK IT centre with William.

I couldn't stop thinking about William and his late wife (June who died in January) and Jerry (who'd met a lively young lady on a cruise) and his daughters Dawn (without a job) and Abigail (with a puppy).

I'd written 'Help a fellow person' on the list without much thought, but something that occurred to me as the summer drew to a close, was that part of the reason I'd been driving myself so crazy was because I'd been so completely self-absorbed. I'd spent weeks and weeks thinking about what experiences I wanted to have and what I wanted to do with my life and how I could be happy.

I, I, I. Me, me, me.

The refreshing thing about the short time I'd spent helping William was that I wasn't thinking about myself at all, just for a while.

It was like what Mum had said about being too busy with her three children and full-time job to worry too much about her calling. Maybe, I reasoned, if I was helping some other people with their problems, I wouldn't be so focused on my own that I'd end up having another self-indulgent existential crisis.

I went back to the IT Centre. This time I actually added my details to the form, and two days later I got a call inviting me to a training day.

It turned out that I should never have let this fairly straightforward hoop put me off, as it actually consisted of nothing more than an hour's briefing with an IT technician on the various idiosyncrasies of the IT set-up, followed by a chat with Linda, the centre manager, about the time commitment I could offer and what to do if anyone got stroppy with me. The following Saturday morning, I headed down to the IT centre for my first session – a fairly gentle ten till twelve shift. I'd asked Linda to let William know I was going to be there. I didn't think he'd be particularly interested, but I felt bad about the way I'd dashed off the last time I'd seen him.

As it turned out, William *was* interested. So much so that he'd made a special trip especially to see me.

'I've been practising, you know. Typing. Still takes me an hour or two for an email but better than four hours! I'm going to email Abigail now. You just watch, I'll have the whole thing done before eleven!'

'That great!' I told him.

And it was, because he did.

Before the end of my shift, I showed William how to use Skype, which his family had told him about but which he assumed would be too technical for him. Dawn, he told me, had just announced she was pregnant, and the thought that he would be able to see the baby on the screen with his own eyes as soon as it emerged, delighted him 'beyond words'.

'It is good of you,' William told me as he gathered his handwritten pages and pens and notebook full of passwords into the carrier bag he kept with him, 'to give up your time like this. I always think, young people these days, they've got better things to be doing, haven't they? Wouldn't you rather be out there, having fun?'

I laughed. 'Sometimes,' I said. 'Sometimes. But not all the time.'

Read on for a sneak peek at what
Gracie gets up to next, in
To Be Perfectly Honest . . .

'For fifty days, I, Grace Georgina Dart,
pledge to be completely, 100% honest
at all times.'

PART 1:

Where we are all living a lie

The Idea of a Party

It was Friday night and I was on my way to a party. This was not a normal Friday night for me.

It wasn't just any party either. It was a warehouse party, on an industrial estate, where an actual DJ would be playing music on actual decks. I was excited by the way it all sounded. It sounded fun and cool and a little bit crazy.

In fact, I was so excited by the idea of the party that I was forcing myself to ignore the part of my brain telling me that the reality might not be quite as good.

I had been to parties before, but I wasn't yet convinced they were for me. I'd heard about good ones happening, but the ones I found myself at always seemed to just be people I didn't know very well sitting around in cramped rooms, talking about nothing and drinking out of plastic cups. And that was basically what we did every day in the canteen anyway. Except, at least in the canteen you could buy chips and we all had our own chair to sit on.

Everyone else was very excited about the location, but I think maybe the industrial estate element was putting me off. Industrial estates were cold and dirty, weren't they? Full of dark shadows and big signs for companies you'd never heard of. They were the kind of place you go with your dad on a Saturday morning to wait in the car in the rain while he talks to a man in overalls about how many bags of cement it takes to make a driveway.

Still, none of this mattered because even if the plan had been to hold the party in a toilet-brush factory, there was still no way I would be missing it. I was only in my second week at Coniston College, for heaven's sake. If I started being the kind of person to turn down party invites in favour of staying at home to watch Gardeners' World with my parents at this delicate stage in my life, I might never shake the label. I might never get invited anywhere again.

I was with Til, my oldest friend, and Reeta, my newest. Til and I had been friends since we were thirteen. Reeta I'd met just two weeks earlier, in my psychology class. The three of us had gathered on the corner at the bottom of the hill outside Til's block of flats, as arranged, to walk up to the party together. Til was wearing what she always wore – black jeans, black boots and a black jumper. Reeta, for some reason, was wearing a rainbow tutu and pink fairy wings.

'It's not fancy dress, is it?' I asked, suddenly alarmed. I hated fancy dress but I hated the idea of being the odd one out more.

'No,' Reeta said, twirling around on the pavement like a ballerina. 'I just like to wear a statement piece.'

Til raised an eyebrow. 'What statement are you making? That you're insane?'

'Til!' I said. I was used to Til's bluntness but I thought it might be a bit early in the friendship to be unleashing it on Reeta like this.

Reeta seemed unfazed though. She just grinned, shrugged, took out a four-pack of Snickers from her bag and ate one in two mouthfuls. Reeta was always eating but her four-times-a-week cross-country running hobby meant that she was still no wider than a lamp-post.

'Energy,' she explained. 'For the rave.'

She offered me one, but I shook my head. I didn't want to turn up at my first industrial warehouse party smelling of peanuts.

'Where are we going then?' I asked Til.

'It's up the hill,' she said. 'Round the corner.' She made a vague swooshing movement with her hand.

'How far is it?' Reeta asked, adjusting her wings as if she might be contemplating flying there.

'Twenty minutes,' Til said. 'Ish.'

Til's idea of twenty minutes, it turned out, was actually nearer fifty, and it was almost completely dark by the time we arrived at the tall wire fence holding a plastic sign saying:

COLDTREE INDUSTRIAL ESTATE

In the four corners of the car park, there were floodlights on poles but they didn't throw out much light. With the tall buildings casting long shadows and the drizzle that had started to fall, the whole place felt more like the set of a Sunday night Victorian murder programme than the scene of a lively social gathering.

Reeta shivered and looked around her. 'Doesn't feel much like a party.'

Til shrugged. 'That's 'cause we're stood in the car park, innit. We're not there yet.'

'So where do we have to go?' Reeta asked.

Til peered at her phone, using her hand to shield the screen from the drizzle. 'It's Unit 2B.'

The host of the party was a boy from college called Archie Dunbar and the music was to be provided by his brother, Lewis, who was a real-life DJ in a real-life club. (On Wednesdays he was, anyway. On the other days he made sandwiches at Subway.) The invite to the party had gone round college like a Mexican wave. You'd hear rumours of it from afar – where it would be and when, stories of how good Archie's parties had been in the past – so by the time someone officially associated with it wandered over and said, 'You should come, if you like. Friday night,' it was hard to stop yourself from kissing them on both cheeks in delight.

'Where is everyone?' Reeta said, pulling her coat on over her front, like a dentist putting on a plastic apron, so as not to interfere with her fairy wings. 'Shouldn't there be people around?'

'We're probably just really early,' I said. 'Or else they're all inside.'

'But inside where?' Reeta said.

'Listen.' Til stopped suddenly and we all stood still, our eyes narrowed as we tried to hear past the sound of the rain, which was getting steadily heavier. 'Hear that?'

There was a rhythmic thump coming from the other side of the car park – the sound of three bassy beats and then a higher crunching sound, in a repetitive pattern.

'Is that the decks?' Reeta asked, wide-eyed. 'Is that what decks sound like?'

Til shrugged. 'It's obviously what these ones sound like.' She pushed her hands into her jacket pockets and strode off towards the sound. Reeta and I followed.

'Yeah, this seems right,' she said as we approached a three-storey building with a corrugated roof. She looked down at her phone and then up at the building again. 'Archie said the warehouse was above a bathroom shop or something . . . and look.' She nodded up towards a sign. Big blue plastic letters spelt out:

WASH STOP

'Sounds like a bathroom shop, right?'

I shrugged.

The music was louder now we were right outside. I could feel it vibrating up my legs.

'I can see people!' Reeta said, excitedly pointing up towards a second-floor window.

As we looked up at the window, a light came on and went off again. Then a figure walked past, then another.

'But how do we get in?' I pulled on the metal door handle but it was locked. 'Are we just supposed to go through the shop or what?'

'Archie said he might need to let us in,' Til said. 'Call him.'

I did as I was told.

Archie took forever to answer the phone. 'You're there already?' he said. 'Bit keen, aren't you?'

I felt my cheeks get warm. No one had told us a specific time. How was one supposed to be fashionably late to a party when no one was very clear about exactly what time was unfashionably early?

'Uh, yeah,' I mumbled. 'We were on our way back from a . . . thing, so we thought we might as well just come now and . . .'

Archie sighed. 'Lewis is there now getting set up, but he won't want anyone up there yet. You can wait downstairs though. He usually sets up like a chill-out area for when it gets a bit much for people, with drinks and snacks and stuff.'

I listened to Archie's directions to this so-called chill-out area, all the time trying not to feel too alarmed by the idea that the party might be the type to get 'a bit much'.

So-Called Chill-Out Area

We headed around the side of the building as Archie had instructed, and after a bit of scrabbling around in the dark, we managed to find the door he'd mentioned. We let ourselves in.

We looked around us. After a few moments, Til said, 'Well, this is OK then. Inside, at least.'

'Yeah,' I agreed. 'It's good to ease in gently, isn't it. Don't want to walk right into a rave off the street.'

The truth was, I was a little disappointed by the chill-out area. I'd had visions of bean bags, fairy lights and wind-chimes. Maybe bubbles floating around gently in front of us from some unseen machine and snacks served on silver trays. But actually the room wasn't even really a room – it was more of a corridor, with a row of wooden benches along one wall and lockers along the other. But then who was I to say what a chill-out area should look like? All my ideas about anything were from the telly.

We sat in silence for a minute, looking around us. The bassy rhythmic music was still going on above us.

'That's what's good about chill-out rooms,' I said, as if I had seen many in my time. 'You can still hear the tunes, but you can talk too.'

I saw Til's eyebrow twitch a little. I think it was because I had said 'tunes'. It had surprised me too, to be honest.

'It's kind of mesmerising,' I said. 'When you let the rhythm in, it really gets to you.'

Reeta nodded her head in agreement. Or in time with the music, I wasn't quite sure.

Another fifteen minutes went by. 'How long do you think we have to wait?' Reeta said. 'How long does the chill-out bit usually last?'

Neither Til nor I replied. Having already been made to feel quite silly about being so keen and early, I didn't fancy calling Archie back to ask. We'd just have to wait till things got going. I hoped it would be worth it.

'I'm so hungry,' Reeta said, her most common announcement. 'I thought Archie said there'd be drinks and snacks in this chill-out area? I can't see any snacks.'

'There's the machine.' Til nodded over to the vending machine, partially stocked with Cokes, Kit-Kats and Wotsits.

'And look,' I said, standing up and going over to a small table at the end of a row of lockers, where there was a bowl of some kind of crispy balls. 'There's food here. I mean, you're not exactly going to get little vol-au-vents and mini burgers – it's not a wedding! It's an industrial warehouse dance party!'

I passed the bowl to Reeta. She peered at the crisps closely, then took a handful and put them in her mouth. She chewed with her head on one side. 'My dad does mountain climbing,' she said, 'and when he's on a trek he has these little packets of cakes that taste a bit funny but they're specially designed to release energy slowly and make your body absolutely ready for climbing. Do you think these are like this?' She looked at me hopefully. 'Do you think at an industrial warehouse dance party they put on special snacks to help you party all night?'

'Probably,' I said. I was starting to feel fairly sure that I wasn't up to partying for even one eighth of the night.

Reeta kept eating until the bowl was almost empty, and we all carried on listening to the thumpy music, and I did actually start to feel quite chilled out in the chill-out area. That was until the door opened, a man in overalls stepped into the room and I sat up straight in alarm.

'Can I help you?' he asked, drying his hands on what looked like a grubby old T-shirt.

'Uh . . .' I looked at him. He looked too old to be at college. In his thirties, at least. But then Archie's brother was older, and who knew how many people had been invited to this enormous wild party. I really didn't think he was dressed for a party though. He looked rather sweaty and dusty.

'We're here for the party . . .' I said. I felt silly for some reason, saying it out loud. 'The party thing, I mean. The warehouse thing . . .'

He frowned. 'You what?'

Til had been lying across the full length of a bench, but she sat up now. 'Is Archie here?' she said. 'Do you know when we can go up?'

The man looked blank and shook his head. 'Archie? No. Nah. Just me and Kev tonight.'

I didn't know this man or 'Kev' but a party with just two people didn't sound like much of a party at all. And where was Lewis, with the decks?

My phone rang and Til picked it up from where I'd left it at the end of the bench. 'Well, we're in the chill-out area, like you told us. Where are you?' She sounded impatient. 'Yeah, we're literally –' She stopped talking suddenly, and turned to me. 'What's the name of this bathroom shop?' She tried to crane her neck to see the sign that was directly above us. 'Wash something?'

'Wash Stop,' the overalls man said, throwing his T-shirt-slash-hand towel over his shoulder. 'It's not a bathroom shop though.'

'What?' I said.

'Wash Stop,' Til said into her phone.

'It's not a shop at all,' overalls man said.

Til looked at him. 'Huh?'

'Wash Stop doesn't sell anything.'

'What is it then?' Reeta asked.

He shrugged. 'Industrial laundrette, innit.'

We looked at each other.

'Archie, is it an industrial laundrette, this place?' Til said into the phone. Then she turned back to overalls man. 'So just to confirm, this building isn't Waterworld, a luxury bathroom design company with a basic but spacious warehouse on the floor above it? A warehouse currently being set up for an all-night dance party?'

'You what?' Overalls man frowned and shook his head. He was getting annoyed now, I could tell. 'I've really got no idea what you're on about, but you kids can't be in here. It's a private building. There's machinery here.'

'Archie definitely said it was a bathroom shop,' Til said, looking at the man out of the corner of her eye like he wasn't to be trusted.

'Yeah. Waterworld is a bathroom shop, ' he said. 'But this isn't Waterworld. This is Wash Stop, the second largest industrial launderette in England. Waterworld – and its no doubt lovely warehouse – is at Birchwood Park.'

'Birchwood Park is miles away!' I said.

He nodded. 'Four or five.'

'If this isn't Waterworld and if Lewis isn't up there sorting out the massive party tunes on his decks, how come we can hear the music?' Reeta said, standing up and putting her hands on her hips. 'How come we can hear the massive party tunes? That music can't be coming from four or five miles away.'

The man pulled a face. 'That's not music. That's the machines.'

'Machines?' I asked, quietly.

'Washing machines. Twenty-five commercial-sized washing machines, working their way through two hundred and thirty-six duvet covers, right at this moment.'

Til and I looked at each other, and then down at the floor.

'But –' Reeta began, but I put my hand on her arm to silence her.

I'd realised what had happened and I didn't want the

man to have to spell it out. What had happened was that for the last forty-five minutes the three of us had been nodding along, appreciating the sweet melody of twenty-five industrial washing machines in operation.

A cat came through the door, and wound itself round the leg of a bench.

'A cat!' Reeta said, her confusion about the music immediately eclipsed. She crouched down on the floor to greet it.

'Rocky,' overalls man said. 'Office cat . . . probably wondering why you're eating his food.' He nodded towards the nearly-empty bowl of snacks next to Reeta. She looked down at the bowl, then at the cat, then back to the bowl again. 'Cat . . . food . . . ?'

The man grinned and shrugged. 'I prefer a Kit-Kat and a cup of tea myself, but each to their own.'

Reeta stood up very slowly, took three deep breaths, then ran outside and vomited vigorously into a bush.

Don't miss the rest of Gracie's comedy moments, in
To Be Perfectly Honest . . .

Coming soon!

Jess Vallance

Jess Vallance works as a freelance writer and lives near Brighton. Her YA novels for Hot Key Books are *Birdy* and *The Yellow Room*.